STANLEY THORNES

LA RETRAITE H

ATKINS ROAD

DESIGN
D&T
MAKE IT!

food technology
for key stage 3

HAZEL KING ■ TRISTRAM SHEPARD

First published in 1999 by:
Stanley Thornes (Publishers) Ltd
Ellenborough House
Wellington Street
Cheltenham
GL50 1YW

A catalogue record of this book is available from the British Library.

ISBN 0 7487 4427 4

Designed and typeset by Carla Turchini
Picture research by John Bailey
Artwork by Tristram Ariss, Hardlines and John Fowler
Printed and bound in Italy by G. Canale & C.S.p.A., Borgaro T.se, Turin

The authors would like to thank the following people who read and commented on the manuscript: Roy Ballam, Margherita Chapman, Louise Davies, Caren Doodson, June Scarborough and Jane Tulloch Special thanks is also due to: Thomas Rotherham College, South Yorkshire; teacher Dianne Williamson and pupils David Kettleborough, Ben Liversidge, Jenna Richardson, Charlene Morriss, Nicola Egan, Hannah Dudziak, Laura Kettleborough, Rosey Ellam, Uman Munir, Jenna Dobson, Alison Cliffe and Wayne Higgins from Oakwood School, Rotherham, for their participation in a photography session; Amita Sharma, Customer Services Advisor, Allied Bakeries; Linda Roberts, Environmental Health Officer, Sheffield City Council; Dr Nigel Dickie, Nutrition Consultant, Heinz Public Affairs Office; Ruth Clark, Manager, Jane Asher Party Cakes; Sarah Heron, Food Press Office, Marks & Spencer; Ellen Yeates, PR Assistant, Cheadle Hughes Partnership

Where specific retailer's and manufacturer's products have been used to illustrate industrial practice they are not intended to imply any endorsement.

The publishers are grateful to the following for permission to reproduce photographs and other copyright material: Allied Bakeries pp. 66, 67; Anthony Blake pp. 84 (top – Bill Double), 114 (PFT Associates), 143 (bottom); ASDA p. 136 (top); BOOTS pp. 44 (top), 50, 76, 110 (right), 138 (left), 139 (bottom) 140 (bottom); British Nutrition Foundation p.16,79; Britstock–IFA pp. 12 (bottom left – Selma), 34 (bottom – ICS/Randy G Taylor), 106 (top – NASA/Erich Bach); Cadbury Ltd p. 134; Cephas pp. 32 (Stuart Boreham), 72 (bottom right – Nick Rock), 74 (bottom left – Nick Rock) 126; Department of Health p. 103 (right); Economatics (Education) Ltd pp. 40, 80 (bottom), 105, 107; Food and Drug Administration p. 47; Ginsters p. 15; H J Heinz Company Ltd pp. 28, 29, 143 (middle); Health p. 105; Health Education Authority p. 44 (bottom); Icecream USA p. 78; Images Colour Library p.7 (bottom right); Intactics International p. 35; Jane Asher Party Cakes Ltd pp. 132, 133; J Allen Cash Photolibrary p. 111(left); Kellogg p. 142; Last Resort Picture Library pp. 72, 100 (top and bottom), 117 (bottom), 120, 121, 124; Marks and Spencer pp. 15, 33, 42, 43; Martyn Chillmaid pp. 6 (middle), 12 (top right), 13 (bottom), 14 (top right, top left and bottom right), 20 (left), 21, 22, 23, 24, 25, 26 (bottom), 30, 36, 38, 49, 53, 56 (top left and bottom left), 58, 60, 61, 62, 69 (top), 70, 71, 74 (top left and bottom right), 75 (left), 77, 80 (top and middle), 81 (left), 82, 87, 95, 97, 98 (right), 109, 115, 118, 126 (right), 128, 129, 130, 137; McVities p. 15; Pictor International pp. 12 (top left), 18 (bottom), 116 (top and middle), 140 (top); Procarton p. 135; Robert Harding Picture Library p. 116 (bottom – BBC Magazines Ltd); Sainsbury's pp. 79, 117 (top); Science Photolibrary pp. 68 (bottom – Rosenfeld Images Ltd), 74 (top right – Astrid and Hanns Frieder Michler), 74 (middle left and middle right – David Scharf), 81 (right – Marcos Lopez), 90 (James Holmes/Farmer Giles Foods), 98 (left – NIBSC); Sheffield City Council pp. 102, 103 (left – Linda Roberts); Still Pictures pp. 6 (bottom – Wolfgang M Weber), 32 (Nigel Dickinson) 72 (right – Helier Mason); Stockmarket p. 96; Tivall pp. 73, 88, 89, 91; Tony Stone Images pp. 12 (top right – Lori Adamski Peek), 72 (bottom left – Alan Thornton), 139 (right – Dennis O'Clair); Topham Picturepoint 111 (right), 126 (left); Wholesnax Ltd p. 15

Every effort has been made to contact copyright holders. The publishers apologise to anyone whose rights have been overlooked and will be happy to rectify any errors or omissions at the earliest opportunity.

Contents

Introduction

Welcome to **Design & Make It! Food Technology for Key Stage 3**. This book will help you succeed in Design and Technology. It tells you all you need to know about working with food as a material when designing and making food products.

How to use this book

The book starts by explaining about Food Technology. It gives examples of the sort of work you can expect. The **Project Guide** which follows will be useful throughout your course. It explains the different design and making aspects of a Food Technology project. You will be assessed on these skills.

The book is then divided into six **units**. Each unit begins by setting you a design challenge. What you will need to do to meet the challenge is explained. The pages which follow will:

▷ tell you what you need to know
▷ set tasks for you to do
▷ remind you how to keep a record of what you do.

Each unit focuses on a different aspect of food technology:

Unit 1 – ingredients and the role they play when designing and making with food.

Unit 2 – diet and health. It considers how to achieve a nutritionally balanced cook–chill meal that matches consumer needs.

Unit 3 – the development of new ideas in food design and production. It looks specifically at bread products.

Unit 4 – food preservation. Food production systems are also investigated.

Unit 5 – hygiene and safety in the food area, for food handlers and in food preparation.

Unit 6 – one-off production and the designing and making of quality food products.

At the end of the book is a **Dictionary**. This is a reference section you will find useful throughout your course. It explains and illustrates special words and phrases often used in Food Technology. Words printed in **red type** in the book are included in this dictionary.

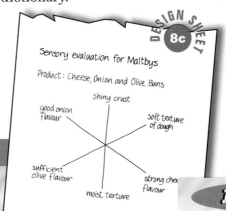

Examples of pupils' work from design sheets are often provided. These will give you a good idea of the sort of work you need to do.

● On task

These sections will set you tasks to do. Sometimes they will be practical. Sometimes they will ask you to find out more about existing food products. Your teacher will tell you which tasks you need to do, and when.

On your design sheet

● These boxes will remind you what you need to put on paper as part of your design folder.

● You will be encouraged to use coloured sketches, charts and diagrams as well as words.

● Where more than one design sheet is used, this is shown as: **8c**

Remember

● These boxes will help you revise what you have learned.

● They provide a summary of the key points you need to know.

What is Food Technology?

Food Technology is one area within the subject called Design and Technology. All areas of Design and Technology involve designing and making products.

In Food Technology you will design and make products using food as your material.

You will learn different ways to prepare, combine, mix and heat ingredients. These skills will help you design and make many different food products.

You will also learn how to store, preserve, cook and package food.

Learning about all these things will help you produce successful, high quality food products.

Food Technology at work

In the food industry food technologists are needed to:

▷ find out exactly what sort of food products people want

▷ discover where and when people want to buy, prepare and eat these products

▷ ensure the food products will be safe to eat

▷ work out how they can be produced and sold at a price people will be willing to pay

▷ calculate how many to make over what period of time.

Designing and making food products

To design and make quality food products the units in this book will help you learn more about:

▷ different food materials such as bread, cereals, fruit, vegetables, eggs, alternative protein foods

▷ different food products, such as snacks, cakes, cook–chill and frozen foods

▷ using and adapting recipes

▷ choosing, preparing and combining ingredients

▷ the physical, chemical and aesthetic properties of food materials and products

▷ evaluating food products using sensory tests.

Design IT! There are opportunities to use computers when designing food products. Find out what software is available in your school.

As you work through the units in this book you can expect to design and make things like:

▷ sweet or savoury snacks

▷ cook–chill meals

▷ sweet or savoury flavoured bread products

▷ alternatives to sandwiches

▷ frozen vegetarian school meals

▷ cakes for special occasions.

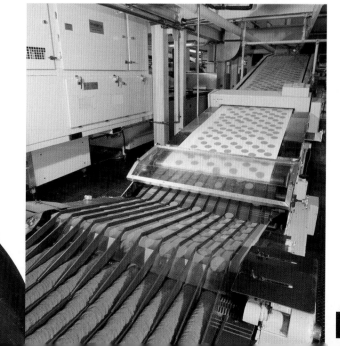

Project Guide

Investigation

To investigate something means to examine, inquire or find out more about it.

In your D&T Food Technology projects you will need to do some investigation to learn more about:
• the consumers you are designing for
• what they need and want
• what the product might be made from and how it might be made.

As you plan and carry out investigation work you need to keep asking yourself whether you are finding out the **right** information. It must be **relevant** to your project.

To do this you will have to:
• observe and talk to your target consumer group
• consult books, leaflets, booklets, etc.
• contact experts for advice
• use CD-ROMs, software and the Internet.

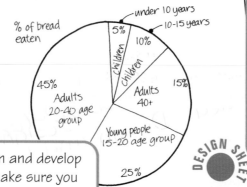

Bread survey

• Which consumer group eats the most flavoured bread products?

% of bread eaten

under 10 years 5%
10–15 years 10%
Children
Children
Adults 40+ 15%
Adults 20–40 age group 45%
Young people 15–20 age group 25%

DESIGN SHEET

As you design and develop your ideas, make sure you take into account the things you have discovered in your investigation.

Have good ideas

Having good ideas of your own is a very important part of work in Design and Technology.
Experiment with different ingredients and methods. Think of lots of possible ideas – don't just choose your first idea.

You also need to think about the **design** specification and the **conflicting demands** within it. Look in the dictionary at the back of this book for more information about these.

New bread product – design ideas

DESIGN SHEET

Sweet
• Individual buns shaped like gingerbread people
white bread dough
cherries
sultanas

Savoury
• Pizza folded and cut into individual portions
wholemeal bread dough
tomato
cheese
bacon
garlic
herbs
Triangles of pizza are

As you design, your ideas will change. Make sure you explain why you decided to change them.

Remember that it is very important to record your ideas on your design sheets. Use words and sketches together. Use colour to help explain your ideas.

Develop your design

As you finalise your design ideas you need to **test them out**. It would be crazy to make 100 snack bars if you hadn't tried the recipe first!

What do you want to learn from your tests? How can you get the information you want?

Ask people from your target consumer group to taste your product and say what they think about it.

Presenting your ideas is very important. Show your notes and sketches to other people, to get their comments and suggestions.

Your work needs to show the features of your design: who it is for, its ingredients and how it would be made.

Apply what you know (designing)

So what **do** you know about working with food? Probably a lot more than you think!

As you work through your food projects you will learn a lot about the **properties** and **characteristics** of the different foods and processes you use.

You will get to know what happens when certain ingredients are combined in different ways.

On your design sheets you need to make it clear how you are applying what you know to your work.

Evaluation

Evaluating food products that already exist will help you understand **how** and **why** they have been designed that way.

You need to do more than just describe an existing product. Comment on its **quality** – how successful it is. Use as many descriptive words as possible.

Use what you have discovered to help you come up with ideas for a new product.

Compare an existing product with other similar products. What do other people say about it? Their views might be different to yours. Include the results of sensory testing.

Evaluate your **own ideas**. On your design sheets record:
• which are your best ideas, and why
• how well your ideas might work
• what you plan to do next as a result of evaluating your own work.

Project Guide

Plan the making

Planning what you are doing is a very important aspect of design and technology project work. There are so many things to do that you have to work out what **order** to do them in, and **how long** to spend doing them.

What needs doing first? What can be done later? How much time do you need to allow for cooling, setting, freezing, etc?

Make a list of all the things you need to do. Try to sort the list into **main stages** of production – preparing the materials, combining them, etc. Then put them in order within each main stage.

Input

DESIGN SHEET

Flour, eggs, sugar
Swiss Roll tin: lined and greased
electric whisk, bowl, sieve
spoon, spatula

Energy – production worker, electric whisk

Where might **difficulties** occur? What would you do if you ran out of a particular ingredient?
At what stages could you check the **quality** of what you are making? Where will you include hygiene checks?

Record your planning work on your design sheets. You may need to change your plans when things don't go as expected. Be sure to explain what you did and why.

Apply what you know (making)

How can you use what you already know about working with food as a material?

From previous work you have done you should know about things such as:
• the dangers of food poisoning
• the need for safety in food preparation areas
• different types of production methods.

This is where you need to make sure you try to choose the best ingredients and tools to make the food product you have designed

You need to match what you know about the characteristics and properties of ingredients with the tools and equipment you know you will be able to use.

Steps in producing a Sausage Double-Decker

Steps	Possible hazards
• collect sausages from storage	• might not be fresh
• separate sausages using sharp knife	• could contaminate other foods

DESIGN SHEET

On your design sheets you need to make it clear how you are applying what you know to your work.

◎ Working with materials

As you make your food products you need to **take care** while you work.

Use the tools carefully to combine ingredients together. Be as **accurate** as you can when you weigh and measure. You will need to organise your tools and your workspace to make your product safely and accurately.

If you are not sure about a particular process it might be a good idea to **practise** it first before you make your final product.

Final design: Melted Brie and Grape Croissant

Hygiene notes

- I left the Brie cheese on the side until I needed it, I should have kept it cool in the fridge (1°C – 4°C)

Pay close attention to **safety** and **hygiene** precautions while you work.

Explain on your design sheets how carefully you worked. Say which safety and hygiene precautions you observed.

◎ Final evaluation

At the end of your project you will need to think very carefully about how well you have done.

First consider the food **product** you have designed and made.
- How **successful** is it?
- Does it solve the problem you were given at the start? If not, why not?
- Did it turn out the way you intended. If not, why not?

How could you **improve** the way you work next time? Which aspects of Design and Technology are you going to **target** in your next project? Discuss with your teacher what you will need to do to show you have made **progress**.

When you tested your final product what did the people it was intended for think? Would they come back for more? Maybe they made some useful suggestions for improvements? How might you change your ideas?
Explain how you tested your final product and what happened.

Finally, how well did **you** work during the project? For example:
- How thorough was your investigation?
- How different were all your ideas?
- How carefully did you plan the making?
- What were your strengths and weaknesses?

Starting Point

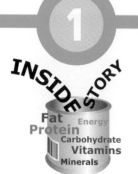

INSIDE STORY

Fat   Energy
Protein
Carbohydrate
Vitamins
Minerals

Many of us lead busy lives. We do not always have time to sit down and eat. We grab small meals or snacks during the day to keep us going. Snacks can be made from sweet or savoury foods.

Can you design and make a sweet or savoury snack which is fun to eat?

Here at Snax we need some help to produce a new snack-type product. It will need to appeal to children who enjoy all sorts of sports.

We will be selling these products at leisure and sports centres. Nutritional information will need to be provided with the snack.

SLUSH PUPPIE

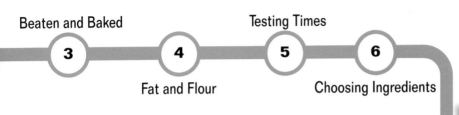

Beaten and Baked
Testing Times

③ ④ ⑤ ⑥

Fat and Flour
Choosing Ingredients

⑧ ⑦

An Interview with...
Heinz
Snack Attacks

The focus

In this unit you will focus on ingredients. This means you will learn about what is inside food, and why we need to eat it. You will find out how ingredients work together when food products are made.

PLUM FRUIT BAR

Vitalinea's plum fruit bars are a deliciously natural approach to wiser snacking. The balanced recipe of fruit and biscuit carbohydrates provide a deliciously sensible and sustaining snack.

Ingredients : Fruit Filling (contains Sugar, Dried Fruit (Plums 10%, Currants, Apple), Dextrose, Glucose Syrup, Stabiliser : Glycerine, Gelling Agent : Pectin, Malic Acid, Flavouring), Wheat Flour, Sugar, Vegetable Oil, Glucose Syrup, Salt, Raising Agents (Ammonium Bicarbonate, Sodium Bicarbonate), Flavouring, Emulsifier : Calcium Stearoyl-2-Lactylate, Dried Whole Egg, Dried Whole Milk.

Jacob's products are baked with care, for your enjoyment. If you are not satisfied, please return the product and its packaging to the address below. Your statutory rights are not affected. Imported by THE JACOB'S BAKERY LIMITED, P.O. BOX 14, LIVERPOOL L9 7JX. All affixed Tredemarks belong to subsidiaries of the DANONE GROUP.

DANONE ™
A DANONE
GROUP COMPANY

NET WEIGHT :
150g ℮

NUTRITION INFORMATION	per 100 g	per BAR
ENERGY	1561 kJ - 370 kcal	515 kJ - 122 kcal
	3.6 g	1.2 g
PROTEIN	71.9 g	23.7 g
CARBOHYDRATE	47.5 g	15.7 g
(of which sugars)	24.4 g	8.0 g
(of which starch)		2.5 g
FAT	7.5 g	1.3 g
(of which saturates)	4.0 g	0.8 g
DIETARY FIBRE	2.3 g	0.1 g
SODIUM	0.18 g	

The challenge

Snax has set you a challenge! Can you design and make a new snack-type product for this food manufacturer?

To meet this challenge you must think carefully about your consumers. You must find out what children like to eat. This will involve testing and evaluating snack products.

The end product

Finally you will design and make an original snack idea for Snax.

To be successful it must:

▶ appeal to children by being fun and tasty to eat

▶ list the nutritional information.

Always keep your target group in mind

Likes and Dislikes

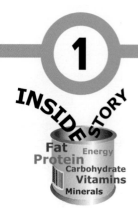

INSIDE STORY

Fat Energy
Protein
Carbohydrate
Vitamins
Minerals

What do you enjoy eating? What do your friends enjoy eating?

Your investigation will begin by finding out which snacks children like and dislike. This is important when designing a new product.

Chocolate or crisps?

After a day at school or a game of sport you probably feel hungry. What sort of food do you like to eat?

Salty, savoury crisps?

Sweet chocolate bars?

Fresh fruit and vegetables?

Do you prefer packets containing several items?

Maybe it depends where you are or who you are with… or just how you feel at the time!

● On task 1

Work with a partner. On design sheet **1a**:

1. List five savoury snacks.

2. List five sweet snacks.

3. Draw grids next to your lists, to make two tables. Look at the example below to help you.

4. Decide which snack you like most. Your favourite snack gets 5 points. Your next favourite snack gets 4 points, and so on.

5. You fill in column A. Your partner fills in column B.

6. Do the same for sweet snacks.

7. Ask three other people to fill in your tables. Add up the scores.

On your design sheet, write down the most popular savoury snack.
Write down the most popular sweet snack.

DESIGN SHEET
1a

Savoury snacks:

	A	B	C	D	E	Total
crisps	1					
pizza	4					
samosa	5					
bombay mix	2					
peanuts	3					

Shops and consumers

Many shops sell snack food. You can buy snacks from:

▷ supermarkets
▷ petrol stations
▷ newsagents
▷ cinemas
▷ sports centres.

Can you think of any others?

People who buy products are called **consumers** Some different types of consumers are shown on the right.

Some snacks are aimed at particular consumers. These consumers are known as the **target group**. In this task your target group is children.

● On task 2

Work as a group or class.

1. Look through some newspapers and magazines. Cut out advertisements for snack foods. Collect wrappers and packets from snack foods.

2. Make a collage of snack pictures. They could be divided into different types: for example, sweet, savoury, sporty, healthy.

3. Choose five snacks from your collage. Write down on design sheet **1b**:

   ▶ which shops might sell them
   ▶ which consumer groups might buy them.

On your design sheets

- Record the snacks children like to eat. **1a**

- Make a collage of snack food advertisements, wrappers and labels. **1b**

- List snacks that are already available and who might eat them. **1b**

Remember

- When designing food products it is important to find out what different people like and dislike.

- New food products are designed for target groups of consumers.

Eat to Live

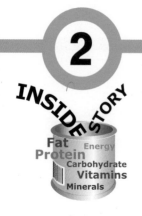

All of us know which foods we enjoy eating. Have you ever stopped to wonder why we eat? What is in food that makes it so important to us?

Nutrients

All foods contain different amounts of **nutrients**. Some contain only a few. Others contain many.

There are five main nutrients:

1. protein
2. carbohydrate (sugar, starch and **NSP** or fibre)
3. fat
4. vitamins (A, B, C, D, E, K)
5. minerals (such as calcium, iron, phosphorus, sodium, zinc).

Your body needs these nutrients every day. It must also have water. When we eat food it is broken down into nutrients. This is known as **digestion**. The nutrients then go to parts of our body where they are needed.

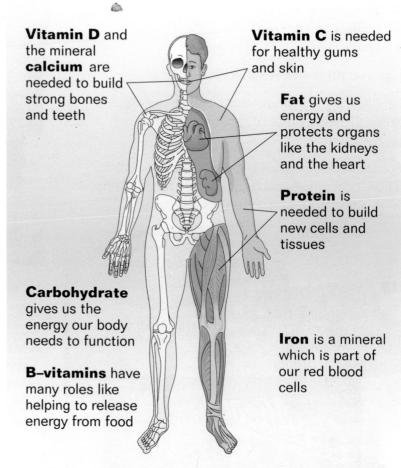

Vitamin D and the mineral **calcium** are needed to build strong bones and teeth

Vitamin C is needed for healthy gums and skin

Fat gives us energy and protects organs like the kidneys and the heart

Protein is needed to build new cells and tissues

Carbohydrate gives us the energy our body needs to function

B–vitamins have many roles like helping to release energy from food

Iron is a mineral which is part of our red blood cells

● On task

Look at the nutrients shown in the diagram above. On your design sheet:

1. Choose three nutrients you think would be important to include in a snack for active children. Give a reason for choosing each one.

2. Use a software package to find out which ingredients provide these nutrients. If a computer is not available, use books instead.

You could present your work in a table like the one shown on the facing page.

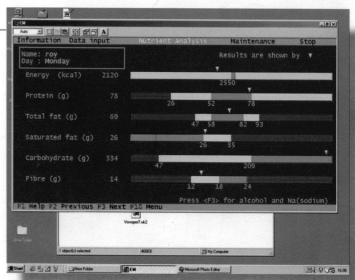

Ingredients

When designing new food products the ingredients must be chosen carefully. One reason is the product may have to provide certain nutrients.

Fruit and vegetables provide vitamins and minerals as well as NSP (dietary fibre) and some carbohydrate

Dairy products provide calcium, protein, B-vitamins and vitamins A and D

These foods provide protein, B-vitamins and the minerals iron, zinc and magnesium

These foods provide the carbohydrates starch and NSP (dietary fibre) as well as calcium and iron and B-vitamins

These foods provide lots of fat ...or fat and sugar ...or just sugar

Remember

- Food contains nutrients.

- The five main nutrients are protein, carbohydrate, fat, vitamins and minerals.

- Designing new food products involves thinking about the nutrients provided by different ingredients.

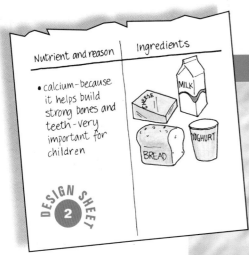

Nutrient and reason	Ingredients
• calcium – because it helps build strong bones and teeth – very important for children	

DESIGN SHEET 2

On your design sheet

- Record the nutrients a new snack for active children could provide.

- Write down why you have chosen them.

- Show which ingredients supply those nutrients.

Beaten and Baked

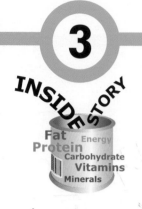

It is important to know what happens to ingredients when making food products. They can be mixed, heated and stirred. They may be beaten, baked and combined with other ingredients.

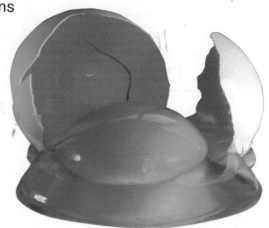

Working ingredients

The way ingredients work in a recipe can depend on their main nutrient. Here are some examples.

Protein

Protein plays an important role during cooking. The protein will set or **coagulate** when foods containing protein are heated.

A good example of this is an egg frying. The egg is poured into a hot frying pan. The egg white quickly changes from runny and clear to solid and white. If cooked for long enough the yolk would set hard too.

Eggs are usually used when making cakes. The egg protein helps the cake to set while the cake mixture bakes.

Other food products containing eggs include:

▷ flans   ▷ sauces   ▷ pastries
▷ biscuits   ▷ mousses   ▷ pancakes
▷ breads   ▷ burgers

Separating egg white and yolk in mass production

Using eggs

How might eggs be used in the preparation of food products?

Eggs trap air when whisked, making food products light

Egg white traps more air than whole egg

Egg can glaze food products like pastry or bread

Eggs thicken some sauces like custards

Eggs coat foods so ingredients like breadcrumbs will stick

Eggs help liquids to set

Eggs stop other ingredients from separating

• On task 1

Work in small groups to carry out these investigations. Each group should write down what happens. Record the results of your investigation on your design sheet. Try to explain why you got the results you did.

Frying eggs

You will need: frying pan, 15 ml (1 tbs) oil, 1 egg, 1 plate, 1 small bowl, spatula.

1. Break the egg into the bowl. Be careful – it must stay whole!
2. Put the oil in the frying pan over a low heat.
3. When the oil is hot, add the egg. Watch what happens.
4. Use the spatula to stop the egg sticking.
5. Write down how the egg changed.

Whisking egg white

You will need: 1 large bowl, electric whisk, saucer and egg cup (or egg separator), 1 egg

1. Separate the egg white from the yolk. Use the egg separator or…
2. Crack the egg onto a saucer. Place the egg cup on the yolk. Tip the egg white into the bowl.
3. Throw away the egg yolk.
4. Whisk the egg white until foamy and firm.
5. Write down how the egg changed.

Whisking whole egg

You will need: 1 large bowl, electric whisk, 1 egg

1. Crack the egg into the bowl.
2. Whisk until thick and foamy.
3. Write down how the egg changed.

Fresh or stale egg?

You will need: 2 plates, 1 fresh egg, 1 stale egg

1. Carefully crack each egg onto a plate. What do you notice? Do not touch the eggs.
2. Draw and label both eggs.

Diagram labels: Thin white, Chalazae, Yolk, Air sac, Thick white

Safety first

These are experiments!
You must not eat the eggs you use.
Raw egg can carry
the bacteria Salmonella.

• On task 2

Each group should report back its results to the class.

▶ Explain exactly what you did.

▶ Describe and show your results.

▶ Explain why you got these results.

Use the information on these pages to help you.

On your design sheet

- Record the results of your investigation using notes and diagrams.

- Explain why you got those results.

Remember

- Protein will set or coagulate when it is heated.

- Eggs have many uses in the preparation of food products.

Fat and Flour

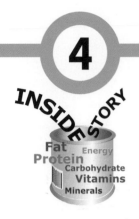

4

INSIDE STORY

Each ingredient has an important role in the preparation of a food product.

Different ingredients, such as fat and flour, also affect the way a food product tastes, looks, smells and feels.

Fat

Margarine, butter and oils are all fats. They are used a lot in cooking. Fats can make food moist. They give it a good flavour and soft texture. Think of the difference between eating dry toast and buttered toast!

Carbohydrate

Flour contains the carbohydrate called **starch**. Flour is used when making bread, biscuits and cakes. It gives the product its bulk or structure.

Flour is also able to thicken other ingredients. To do this it needs liquid and heat. Many sauces are thickened in this way.

How does flour thicken a sauce?

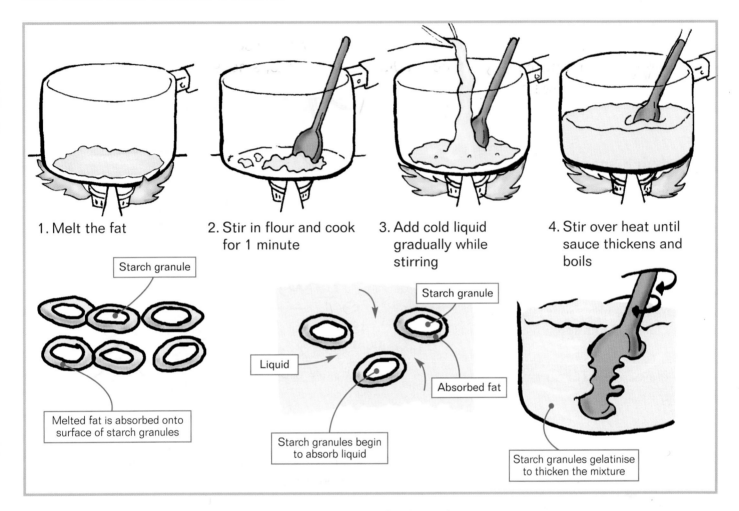

1. Melt the fat

2. Stir in flour and cook for 1 minute

3. Add cold liquid gradually while stirring

4. Stir over heat until sauce thickens and boils

Starch granule

Melted fat is absorbed onto surface of starch granules

Starch granule

Liquid

Absorbed fat

Starch granules begin to absorb liquid

Starch granules gelatinise to thicken the mixture

Sauce flour

Sauce flour is a recently developed product. It has been made using special milling techniques. It is a fine powder. It can be added directly to hot liquids to thicken them. This cannot be done with ordinary flour without lumps forming.

● On task

Investigate making a sauce. Discover how flour thickens liquids by making a savoury snack that uses a sauce. Choose a suitable recipe, or follow one your teacher gives you.

Show clearly what you did on your design sheet.

On your design sheet

- Record how you made a sauce using notes and diagrams.

Remember

- Fat can add flavour and texture to food products.

- Flour contains starch which can thicken liquids when heated.

Testing Times

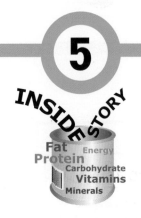

Sandwiches are popular snacks. Designing a new snack could involve looking at sandwiches in a different way.

A sandwich snack

Sandwiches can contain several nutrients including protein, carbohydrate and fat. This depends on their ingredients.

Sandwiches are quick to prepare. If the ingredients are chosen carefully they could make a suitable snack for active children. Remember, your task is to design a snack for children using a sports centre.

Sandwiches are easy to eat, but are they exciting?

● On task 1

This new type of sandwich can be baked in the oven. You have been asked to test the recipe by preparing the sandwich. You will have to prepare a report on your results.

1. Look at the filling ideas in the test recipe on the right. Discuss with a partner what you think of them.

2. Discuss what you will choose as your sandwich filling.

3. Read through the test recipe carefully.

4. On design sheet **5a** make a list of the ingredients you will need to make your sandwich.

Baked Sandwiches

Ingredients
2 thick slices of bread
margarine or butter
30 ml (2 tbs) milk
1 egg
salt and black pepper

Filling ideas
- slices of cheese and tomato
- slices of ham with pickle
- peanut butter
- grilled bacon
- fried mushroom and onion

Method
1. Light the oven at gas mark 6 or switch to 180°C.
2. Use some of the margarine or butter to grease the bottom and sides of an ovenproof dish or sandwich tin.
3. Place one slice of bread in the dish and lay or spread the filling on top.
4. Lightly spread some margarine or butter over the other slice of bread. Use this to make the top of the sandwich (butter side up).
5. Measure the milk into a measuring jug. Crack the egg and add to the milk. Add salt and pepper. Whisk together using a fork.
6. Slowly pour the mixture over the sandwich, pressing down on the bread with the fork so it soaks into the bread.
7. Carefully place the dish at the top of the oven for 20 minutes. The sandwich should be lightly browned and the egg mixture should be set.
8. Remove from the oven. Use a slice to lift the sandwich and transfer to a plate.

Would this sandwich appeal to you?

TEST RECIPE REPORT SHEET

Name of product being tested:

_____

Ingredients used:

_____

Ingredients — any changes needed? Why?

_____

Comments about equipment used:

_____

Method — any changes needed? Why?

_____

Cooking times/temperatures — any changes needed? Why?

_____

Would the snack be suitable for Snax? Give reasons.

A suitable snack

A test recipe may work very well. However, it must suit the target group. While you make your baked sandwich ask yourself, would it be a suitable snack for active children to buy in a sports centre?

● On task 2

1. On design sheet **5a** sketch your baked sandwich filling idea. Label the ingredients. State the main nutrients provided by each. The example shown here might help you.

2. Make your baked sandwich idea.

3. Use the test recipe report sheet on the right to evaluate your finished sandwich. Write the results on design sheet **5b**.

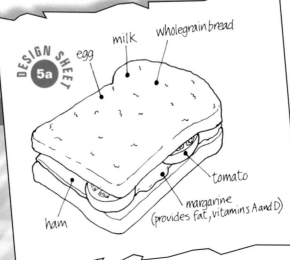

DESIGN SHEET 5a

egg   milk   wholegrain bread

tomato

margarine (provides fat, vitamins A and D)

ham

On your design sheets

- List the ingredients used in your baked sandwich idea. **5a**

- Show the main nutrients in your baked sandwich idea. **5a**

- Fill in your test recipe report sheet. **5b**

Remember

- Design ideas must be tested to make sure they work.

- Design ideas must be liked and wanted by consumers who might buy them.

Choosing Ingredients

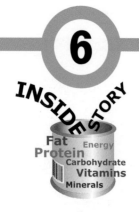

6
INSIDE STORY

Choosing the right ingredients is very important when designing new food products.

Snax would like to know why these ingredients are used to make muffins. What can you tell them?

Muffins

The muffins shown here are American muffins. They have become a popular snack food in Britain. They are easy to make and come in sweet or savoury varieties.

Basic ingredients

Muffins can be made in many different flavours – chocolate, fruit, cheese, or even courgette. Recipes vary, but here are the basic ingredients:

▷ self-raising flour   ▷ milk
▷ baking powder   ▷ oil
▷ sugar   ▷ eggs.

The function of ingredients

Flour:
► adds 'bulk'
► helps muffins to rise

Sugar:
► adds sweetness
► gives brown colouring

Baking powder:
► helps muffins to rise

Milk:
► helps muffins to rise (when heated, milk gives off steam which helps muffins rise)

Oil:
► adds moisture
► adds flavour
► helps prevent drying out (staling)

Eggs:
► help muffins set in the oven (the protein coagulates or sets when heated)

Added nutrients

Each ingredient used in muffins will provide nutrients. Here are the main nutrients provided by basic muffins:

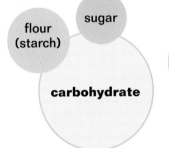

flour (starch) — sugar — **carbohydrate**

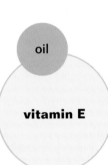

eggs — **protein** — milk

oil — **vitamin E**

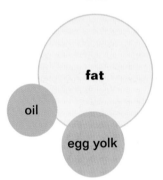

fat — oil — egg yolk

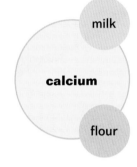

milk — **calcium** — flour

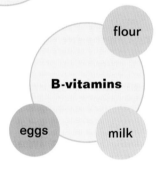

flour — **B-vitamins** — eggs — milk

● *On task*

Investigate making your own muffins. Use the recipe provided by your teacher.

While you are making your own muffins, make notes about what you are doing.

If possible, give reasons on your design sheet why you do what you do. For example: 'I sieved the flour to add air to the mixture. This will make my muffins light.'

Making Banana and Oat Muffins

DESIGN SHEET 6

- When sieving the flour and baking powder I made sure I lifted the sieve up high so lots of air would get trapped in the flour.

- After measuring the milk in the measuring jug I could just add the oil, vanilla and egg – I didn't need another bowl, I beat them together in the jug!

On your design sheet

- Write down the notes you made when making your muffins.

Remember

- Ingredients are chosen in recipes because of their function.

- Recipe methods must be written carefully so the food products are always successful.

Snack Attacks

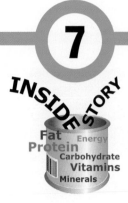

Fat Energy Protein Carbohydrate Vitamins Minerals

Snax is also considering a banana and oat muffin as a new snack. The company would like nutritional information to go on the product label. Can you help?

Label law

Look at the packet of muffins shown on the right. The information on the label is not very helpful, is it? Some of it is not true. Anyone expecting four muffins will be disappointed! Some information is vague. What are the 'other things' in the ingredients list?

Everything written on a food label must be accurate. Manufacturers can be taken to court if a consumer is misled by the labelling. The law has decided certain information must be on every label. These are **legal requirements**.

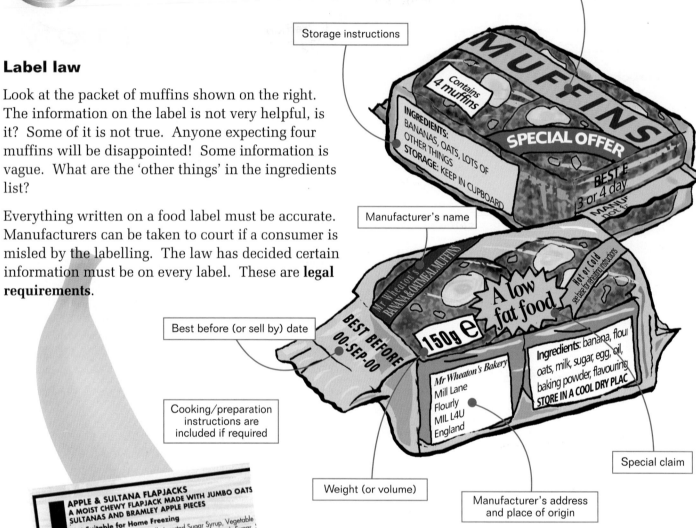

Name of product

Storage instructions

Contains 4 muffins

MUFFINS

SPECIAL OFFER

BEST E 3 or 4 day

INGREDIENTS: BANANAS, OATS, LOTS OF OTHER THINGS STORAGE: KEEP IN CUPBOARD

Manufacturer's name

Mr Wheaton's BANANA & OATMEAL MUFFINS

A low fat food

Hot or Cold see label for reheating instructions

150g ℮

Best before (or sell by) date

BEST BEFORE 00-SEP-00

Mr Wheaton's Bakery Mill Lane Flourly MIL L4U England

Ingredients: banana, flour oats, milk, sugar, egg, oil, baking powder, flavouring STORE IN A COOL DRY PLAC

Special claim

Cooking/preparation instructions are included if required

Weight (or volume)

Manufacturer's address and place of origin

Additional information

Some manufacturers like to add other information to help consumers.

The label might show serving suggestions or the price. Nutritional information is often given. This is not required by law, unless a special claim is made (such as *high in fibre* or *low fat*).

APPLE & SULTANA FLAPJACKS
A MOIST CHEWY FLAPJACK MADE WITH JUMBO OATS SULTANAS AND BRAMLEY APPLE PIECES

Not Suitable for Home Freezing

(i) INGREDIENTS: Oats, Partially Inverted Sugar Syrup, Vegetable Emulsifier: Polyglycerol Esters of Fatty Acids, Flavourings), Sugar, Bramley Apples, Glucose Syrup, Bramley Apple Purée, Modified S Acidity Regulators (Citric Acid, Sodium Citrate), Gelling Agent (So Malic Acid, Calcium Phosphate, Preservative (Potassium Sorbate),

WARNING: This product may contain traces of nuts.

STORE IN A COOL DRY PLACE AND ONCE OPENED IN AN AIRTIGHT CONTAINER.

(Q) TESCO QUALITY: We are happy to refund or replace any Tes falls below the high standard you expect. Just ask any member of This does not affect your statutory rights.

Produced in the U.K. for Tesco Stores Ltd., Cheshunt EN8 9SL, U.K

© Tesco '97 3524

4?

BEST BEFORE: SE

NUTRITION			
TYPICAL COMPOSITION	A 52g (1¾ oz) serving provides	100g (3½ oz) provide	
Energy	930 kJ/222 kcal	1789 kJ/426 kcal	
Protein	2.7 g	5.1 g	
Carbohydrate	32.0 g	31.0 g	
of which sugars	16.1 g	17.7 g	
	9.2 g	6.6 g	
Fat	3.5 g	6.1 g	
of which saturates	3.2 g	1.8 g	
mono-unsaturates	0.9 g		
polyunsaturates	1.4 g	2.7 g	
Fibre	0.1 g	0.2 g	
Sodium			
	This Pack contains 8 servings		
INFORMATION			

5 031021

Know your nutrients

People like to read nutritional labels. They might want to find out the number of calories in the food. Or they might want to know how much fat it contains. This can be very important for people on special diets, such as low fat, high fibre or low salt.

● **On task**

1. Use the recipe shown on the right to work out the nutrients provided by the muffins (per 100 g). Use nutritional software or books.

2. Use a graph or table to present the nutritional information on your design sheet. If possible use a spreadsheet package.

3. Read through the interview with Heinz on pages 28 and 29.

4. If you have time, you could plan a complete label for the muffins.

Banana and Oat Muffins

Ingredients

200 g (7 oz) self-raising wholemeal or white flour
75 g (3 oz) jumbo oats
7.5 ml (1½ tsp) baking powder
50 g (2 oz) soft dark sugar
225 ml (8 fl oz) semi-skimmed milk
60 ml (4 tps) sunflower oil
5 ml (1 tsp) vanilla flavouring
1 medium egg
225 g (8 oz) peeled banana (about 2 medium)

Method

1. Turn on the oven to 220°C/gas 7.
2. Place 10–12 muffin cases in tins (or 18–20 cake cases).
3. Sieve the flour and baking powder in the bowl.
4. Add the oats and sugar. Stir.
5. Measure the milk into a jug; add oil, vanilla and egg.
6. Beat together with a fork. Add to the bowl.
7. Mash the banana and add to the bowl.
8. Mix together gently. Spoon into cases.
9. Bake for 20–25 minutes.

DESIGN SHEET 7

Nutritional analysis of banana and oat muffins

(pie chart with segments labelled: carbohydrate starch, sugar, fat, potassium, vitamin A, vitamin D, calcium, iron, protein)

Banana and Oat Muffins
Nutritional value per 100g

On your design sheet

● Present the nutritional information about the muffins in a suitable way for Snax.

Remember

● The law says labels must show certain information.

● Manufacturers may add other information to help consumers.

● Nutritional labels help people on special diets.

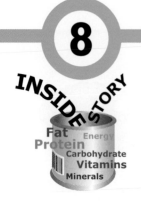

An Interview with...

Heinz was one of the first food companies to introduce detailed nutritional labelling. The information here should help you produce a label for your new snack product.

Heinz has always taken nutrition seriously. It supports the consumers' right to know. Heinz introduced full nutritional labelling before Government guidelines in 1986.

What information can be found on your nutritional labels?

" All Heinz varieties include nutritional information showing the content of the product in relation to energy, protein, carbohydrate, sugars, fat, saturates, sodium and dietary fibre. Information is given per 100g as well as the amount contained in an average serving. "

Suitable for a Gluten Free Diet

HEINZ
The Original
TOMATO KETCHUP

- No starch thickeners, artificial colours, flavours or preservatives are added to Heinz Ketchup.
- The rich, red colour and real tomato taste come only from specially selected tomatoes.
- Our subtle blend of spices - a seasoning secret for over 100 years - makes Heinz Tomato Ketchup the favourite all the family love. Thick, rich and delicious - there's no Ketchup quite like Heinz.

H9369300004

NUTRITION INFORMATION		
TYPICAL VALUES	PER 100g	PER SERVING (10 ml)
ENERGY	429kJ 101kcal	47kJ 11kcal
PROTEIN	1.1g	0.1g
CARBOHYDRATE	24.0g	2.6g
(of which sugars)	(23.4g)	(2.6g)
FAT	0.1g	Trace
(of which saturates)	(Trace)	(Trace)
FIBRE	0.6g	0.1g
SODIUM	1.2g	0.1g

In correspondence please quote quality code on cap

Do you have to provide nutritional labels by law?

" Where a nutritional claim is made then products must, by law, include nutritional information. "

HEINZ

HEINZ POTATO SALAD IS MADE TO A POPULAR HEINZ RECIPE WITH POTATO CHUNKS AND CHIVES IN A DELICIOUS DRESSING. IT IS COMPLETELY FREE FROM ARTIFICIAL COLOURS, FLAVOURS AND PRESERVATIVES. READY TO SERVE EITHER CHILLED OR STRAIGHT FROM THE CAN. FOR A TASTY LIGHT MEAL, IDEAL SERVED MIXED WITH TUNA CHUNKS.
EMPTY OUT UNUSED CONTENTS, COVER, KEEP COOL

INGREDIENTS: POTATOES, WATER, SPIRIT VINEGAR, VEGETABLE OIL SUGAR, ONIONS, MODIFIED CORNFLOUR, MUSTARD, SALT, CHIVES EGG WHITE, STABILISERS - XANTHAN GUM AND GUAR GUM FLAVOURING, HERB EXTRACT, SPICE, COLOUR - BETA-CAROTENE
SUITABLE FOR A GLUTEN FREE DIET
GUARANTEE: Price refunded, without affecting your statutory rights, if any Heinz variety fails to please. In correspondence please quote quality code on can end

NUTRITION INFORMATION		
Typical values	Amount per 100g	Amount per serving (65g)
Energy	590kJ/141kcal	383kJ/92kcal
Protein	1.4g	0.9g
Carbohydrate	14.8g	9.6g
(of which sugars)	(4.3g)	(2.8g)
Fat	8.5g	5.5g
(of which saturates)	(0.6g)	(0.4g)
Fibre	0.8g	0.5g
Sodium	0.5g	0.3g

INGREDIENTS
Beans, Water, Tomatoes, Sugar, Salt
Modified Cornflour, Spirit Vinegar
Spice Extracts, Herb Extract

NUTRITION INFORMATION		
Typical Values	Amount per 100g	Amount per Can
Energy	312kJ/75kcal	640kJ/154kcal
Protein	4.7g	9.6g
Carbohydrate	13.6g	27.9g
(of which sugars)	(6.0g)	(12.3g)
Fat	0.2g	0.4g
(of which saturates)	(Trace)	(0.1g)
Fibre	3.7g	7.6g
Sodium	0.5g	1.0g
Per Can:	154 Calories	0.4g Fat

For free Nutrition Labelling booklet write to:
Heinz Nutrition Service at the address on the back of this can.

HEINZ BAKED BEANS
in tomato sauce

HEINZ BAKED BEANS with **8 Pork Sausages** in tomato sauce
57 VARIETIES

Why do you think nutritional labels are important?

" Consumers have a right to know what they are eating. With increasing consumer awareness about healthy eating it makes sense for information to be given which can help all of us make healthier choices. "

What advice would you give someone planning a food label?

" Make sure it is clear and easy to read. Make sure it is designed so consumers can find the information they want easily. "

Do you know whether your customers use your nutritional labels?

" All our research indicates that many consumers value the information. Information about calories and fat is particularly helpful. "

On your design sheet

- When you design your own snack for Snax you will need to provide nutritional information. You could show how this nutritional information would appear on the product label.

Snack Evaluation

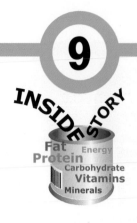

INSIDE STORY

Fat Energy
Protein
Carbohydrate
Vitamins
Minerals

The final challenge for this unit is to make and evaluate your snack idea.

Will Snax be happy to sell it to children in leisure and sports centres?

A new snack

By now you will have investigated snacks and found out what children like to eat. You will also have made some snack products, liked baked sandwiches and muffins.

Remember the challenge that Snax set you:

▷ Design and make a new snack-type product that is fun for children to eat.

▷ It must be suitable for sale in leisure and sports centres.

▷ The product will need nutritional information.

● On task 1

1. Use the information you have learnt about ingredients, nutrients and making food products. Which of these snack products do you think might be a good idea for Snax?
   ► a type of sandwich?
   ► a savoury product?
   ► a sweet or savoury muffin?

2. Write down your chosen recipe on design sheet **9a**.

3. Label any changes you make (such as to the ingredients, methods, cooking times or temperatures). Explain why you made each change.

4. Write down why you think Snax will approve of your new product. Will it:
   ► be easy to eat?
   ► be a suitable portion size?
   ► provide high energy?
   ► appeal to children?

Final evaluation

After making your new snack idea you must evaluate the results. This means you need to decide how well your product meets Snax's challenge.

● On task 2

Use the evaluation chart on design sheet **9b**. Fill in the comments column.

EVALUATION OF NEW SNACK PRODUCT

Product name:
_____

How well do you think the snack will appeal to children? Would they find it fun and tasty to eat?

_____

Describe the snack's:
· taste
· texture
· appearance.

_____

What makes it suitable for sale in leisure and sports centre?

_____

How well does your snack meet the nutritional needs of your target consumer group? Refer to the nutritional information you have provided.

On your design sheets

● Record your recipe. **9a**

● Explain the changes you have made. **9a**

● Say why you think Snax will like your idea. **9a**

● Complete your snack evaluation. **9b**

Remember

● Evaluating food products is important to make sure the design does what is required.

Starting Point

People do not always think about the food they eat. However, food plays a very important role in our lives. Some people do not have enough to eat. Others have more than they need. Everyone should be aiming for a balanced diet.

The challenge

This challenge is going to involve finding out about balanced meals. You will also have to investigate different rice and potato dishes. Your new product will need to be reheated safely too.

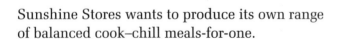

SUNSHINE STORES

Sunshine Stores wants to produce its own range of balanced cook–chill meals-for-one.

▷ These meals must contain rice or potato.
▷ They will be sold from chill cabinets in the stores.

Can you design and make a healthy, tasty one-portion meal for Sunshine Stores?

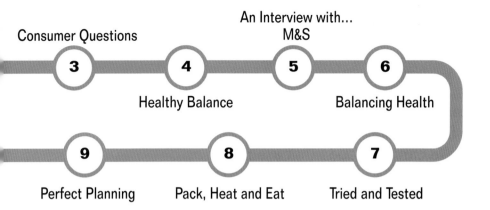

Consumer Questions

3 — **4** — **5** — **6**

An Interview with...
M&S

Healthy Balance

Balancing Health

9 — **8** — **7**

Perfect Planning

Pack, Heat and Eat

Tried and Tested

The focus

To design a new cook–chill meal you will need to look in supermarkets. The chill cabinets will contain many cook–chill meals and products. In the interview on pages 42 and 43 Marks and Spencer will help by telling you about cook–chill products in their 'healthy eating' range.

The end product

After testing ideas for a new product you will make your final meal. It must match the task set by Sunshine Stores below.

SUNSHINE STORES
New Product Specification

The product must:

- be a main meal ☐
- contain rice or potato ☐
- contain a balance of ingredients ☐
- be sold from the chill cabinet ☐

Supermarket Survey

Food shopping often used to be a daily activity. Now we can store food products at home for days, weeks or months. We can buy foods that are partly or completely prepared for us. There is also a wide choice of food products.

Meat in middle so people can browse

Chill cabinets along walls, best area for controlling temperature

Dairy products, juices and c...

Desse...

Fresh meat

Delicatessen

Eggs, salt, etc.

Bisc...

Fresh fish

Ready meals

Confectionery

Vegetables

Fruit and salad

Shopping for food

Buying food used to involve walking from shop to shop. Meat was bought from the butcher, fruit and vegetables from the greengrocer, and so on.

Today it is more usual to go to one place to buy everything. Supermarkets are often 'out of town' so people drive or catch a bus. All sorts of items are sold in supermarkets, from artichokes to alcohol, tomatoes to toothpaste. You can even make shopping a social event by having a meal in the coffee shop.

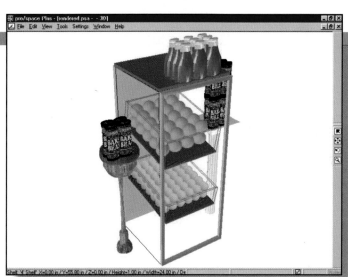

Shopping around

Supermarkets stock many items. Not all of them are food. How do managers decide where to put them in the store?

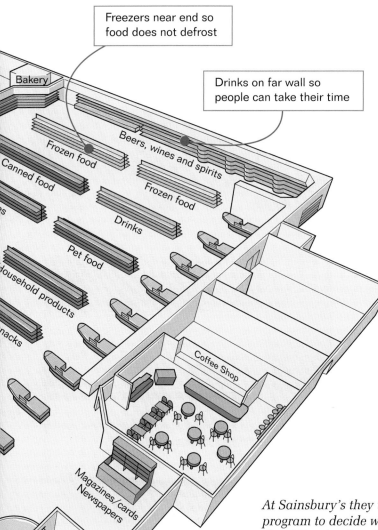

Freezers near end so food does not defrost

Drinks on far wall so people can take their time

Bakery

Frozen food

Beers, wines and spirits

Canned food

Frozen food

Drinks

Pet food

Household products

snacks

Coffee Shop

Magazines/cards Newspapers

Store Entrance

At Sainsbury's they use a special computer program to decide where on the shelf each item should be displayed. The picture shows the layout of a typical Sainsbury's store.

● *On task*

Sunshine Stores want a cook–chill product that contains rice or potatoes. First think about rice dishes.

1. Look through recipes in magazines, books, software and the Internet. You may find meals like risotto, paella, stuffed peppers or fried rice.

2. Choose three ideas for rice dishes. How can you make them fit this task? Write down on your design sheet the ingredients and quantities needed. You may like to use sketches.

3. Choose one rice dish to make. This will help you find out more about cooking with rice.

4. Make your rice dish. Note how rice is cooked.

5. Investigate your local supermarket. What sort of meals and foods are sold in the chill cabinets? Record this on your design sheet.

On your design sheet

● Record your three rice dishes.

● Make notes to show what you have learnt about cooking rice.

● Record your supermarket investigation.

Remember

● Supermarkets provide a wide choice of items, all in one store.

● Computer software can be used to decide where to display each item.

● Chill cabinets contain a variety of food products.

Evaluate the Range

2

Many supermarkets sell products with a 'healthy' image. Some of these may be found in chill cabinets. Here you will take apart and evaluate some cook–chill products. Just how good are they?

Looking at the range

Food products in the 'healthy' range usually claim to be low in fat, sugar, salt or energy. Some may also say they are 'high in fibre'. Products that may be part of a healthy range include yoghurts, biscuits, cakes, drinks, meals and desserts.

Looking at the labels

● *On task 1*

1. Product analysis or 'taking food apart' may involve the study of food labels. Work as a class or group. Look closely at the cook–chill product labels from a 'healthy' range. Find out more about each product by answering the following questions.

- ► What is the product called?
- ► How is it described?
- ► What is the healthy eating claim?
- ► How much does it weigh?
- ► How much does it cost?
- ► How many grammes of fat does it contain per 100g
- ► What is the energy value per 100g in kJ or kcal?

2. Look at your answers so far. Which product would you choose to buy? Why?

Record your work on design sheet **2a**.
Sunshine Stores will want to know the results of your investigation.

Taste testing

Evaluating existing food products will help you design a new cook–chill product.

● On task 2

It would be unwise to judge a food product by the label alone. Working as a class or in groups, carry out the following taste test on two cook–chill products.

1. Carefully read the reheating instructions.

2. Reheat both products.

3. When thoroughly reheated, turn out onto separate plates.

4. Discuss the following:

 ► What do you think of the portion size? How many should it serve? Would it be filling?

 ► Describe the appearance and presentation of the product.

 ► Taste the product. Describe the flavours, textures and aromas (smells).

5. Complete the taste testing table on design sheet **2b**.

6. Note on your design sheet how you can use this information to improve your own design.

On your design sheets

● Record your product label answers. **2a**

● Record your taste test results. **2b**

● Make notes to show how you can improve your ideas now you have evaluated other products. **2b**

Safety first!

Cook–chill products must be thoroughly reheated to kill all food poisoning bacteria. Food should reach 72°C in the centre.

Products for taste testing are given codes or symbols. Their brand names are not used. Tasters should not feel one product is more important than the rest.

TASTE TESTING

	PRODUCT 1	PRODUCT 2
Name of product		
Portion size	Too small	
Appearance	Size is disappointing, but looks quite tasty	
Aroma	Makes you feel hungry	
Taste	Quite sweet for a savoury meal	
Texture	Smooth; nothing to bite on.	

Looking at labels

Label 1

DESIGN SHEET 2a

The product is called Gnocchi with Parmesan.

It is described as....
 Little dumplings made from potatoes, flour and egg, served in a buttery sauce with parmesan topping

Remember

Evaluating existing food products involves:

● taking food apart (product analysis)

● looking at labels

● judging the taste, texture, appearance and aroma of the food.

Consumer Questions

3

Before designing a product for consumers you must ask them what they want. But you need to know who and what to ask!

Sunshine Stores has already carried out some consumer research. It has discovered there is a need for a balanced meal for one. The meal must contain rice or potatoes.

Who to ask

You need to find out which consumers will be your target group. Could your meal be a low-fat dish for healthy eaters? Or something suitable for older people? Sometimes families all eat at different times – perhaps your meal-for-one would suit a child?

What to say

A **survey** is one way to find out what your target group wants. A survey can be carried out using a questionnaire.

Your questionnaire should start with an introduction. People like to know why they are being asked questions! You could say the survey is for Sunshine Stores. Here is an example of an introduction:

Asking questions

A questionnaire contains some carefully worded questions. The questions may be answered *yes* or *no*. Sometimes there is a choice of answers. For example:

How would you describe yourself?

Meat eater	❏	Vegetarian	❏
Vegan	❏	Eat poultry only	❏
Eat fish only	❏	Do not eat red meat	❏

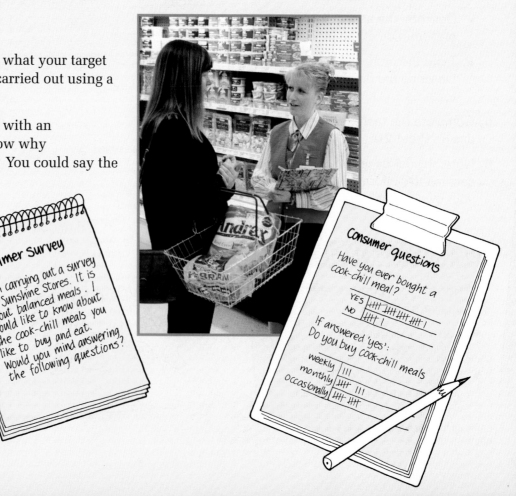

Consumer Survey

I am carrying out a survey for Sunshine Stores. It is about balanced meals. I would like to know about the cook-chill meals you like to buy and eat. Would you mind answering the following questions?

Consumer questions

Have you ever bought a cook-chill meal?

YES	⊞⊞ ⊞⊞ ⊞⊞ I
NO	⊞⊞ I

If answered 'yes':
Do you buy cook-chill meals

weekly	III
monthly	⊞⊞ III
occasionally	⊞⊞ ⊞⊞

Finding things out

Before writing your questions you need to decide what you want to find out. For example, if you design a meal containing meat, you need to know which meat is most popular. You could ask:

Which is your favourite type of meat or poultry? (tick one box)

Beef	❑	Ham	❑	Turkey	❑
Bacon	❑	Pork	❑	Chicken	❑
Lamb	❑	Liver	❑	None	❑

Things you might want to find out include:

▷ the types of meal your target group prefers

▷ if people prefer potato or rice

▷ how often they buy cook–chill meals

▷ how much they would spend on a meal-for-one

▷ how they usually reheat cook–chill meals (microwave or cooker?)

● On task 1

1. Write an introduction for your survey on design sheet **3a**.

2. Write out some questions (in rough) for a questionnaire. Use tick boxes for the answers. Ask your teacher to check them.

3. Write or print your questions underneath your introduction.

4. Carry out your survey.

The results

Following a survey the answers need to be looked at carefully.

The results of a questionnaire should help when designing new products. For example, most people might prefer to eat chicken with rice. So, new ideas should contain chicken and rice!

● On task 2

1. When your survey is complete, look carefully at the results. If possible, use a computer to present your results. Use graphs or tables where appropriate.

2. Make notes about the things you must consider when designing your balanced meal-for-one.

Present your results and notes clearly on design sheet **3b**.

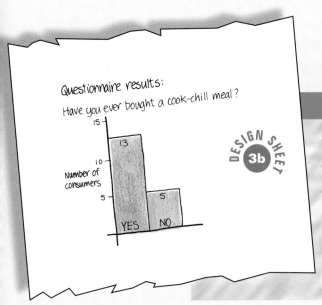

Questionnaire results:
Have you ever bought a cook-chill meal?

DESIGN SHEET 3b

On your design sheets

● Present your questionnaire. **3a**

● Present your results. **3b**

● Make notes about the things you need to consider when designing your new product. **3b**

Remember

● A questionnaire is a useful way to find out what consumers want.

Healthy Balance

4

Eating a balanced diet involves eating a variety of foods, especially fruit and vegetables. This healthy balance must be considered when designing new products.

Food energy

Food provides the body with nutrients and energy. The energy supplied by food is measured as kilojoules (kJ) or kilocalories (kcal).

People need to eat different amounts of food. This is because they require different amounts of energy.

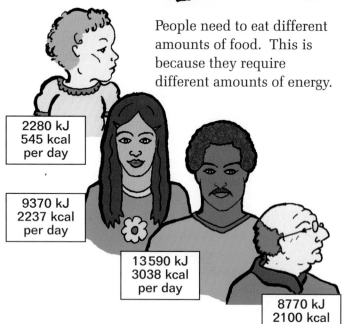

2280 kJ
545 kcal
per day

9370 kJ
2237 kcal
per day

13590 kJ
3038 kcal
per day

8770 kJ
2100 kcal
per day

A very busy, active person may need more food energy. An inactive person may need less food energy. People also require different amounts of energy at different stages of their lives.

● On task 1

How much energy do you need? Use a computer program or books to find out how much energy you might need in one day. Show this on your design sheet.

		Energy Kcal	Fibre g	Protein g	Fat g	Iron mg	Calcium mg
100.0 g	Wheat flour white plain	341.00	3.10	9.40	1.30	2.00	140.00
75.0 g	Cheddar average Cheese	309.00	0.00	19.13	25.80	0.23	540.00
10.0 g	Vegetable oil blended average	89.90	0.00	0.10	9.99	0.10	0.10
100.0 g	Tomatoes raw	17.00	1.00	0.70	0.30	0.50	7.00
20.0 g	Olives in brine	20.80	0.58	0.18	2.20	0.20	12.20
5.0 ml	Sugar white	19.70	0.00	0.05	0.00	0.05	0.10
5.0 ml	Salt table	0.00	0.00	0.00	0.00	0.01	1.45
75.0 ml	Water	0.00	0.00	0.00	0.00	0.00	0.00
5.0 ml	Yeast bakers dried	8.45	0.00	1.78	0.08	1.00	4.00
	Total for Recipe / Menu	805.85	4.68	31.24	39.87	4.09	704.85

Back to Recipe

Advanced Data

DRV's etc...

Print

Page 1 of 2

Click the Vertical Scroll bar to cycle through Foods

Food Name

This is the analysis for 1 person.

Click the Horizontal Scroll bar at this end to view Page Two

UK Nutrient Databank (c) The Royal Society of Chemistry and Crown 1978 through 1991
The Databank includes Crown copyright material (c) Crown copyright 1978 through 1991

Healthy energy

An 11-year-old boy needs about 9270 kJ (2220 kcal) in one day. By eating 362.5 g of peanut butter he could get all the energy he needs. But would this be a balanced diet?

No. A single food cannot provide all the nutrients needed. This is why a varied diet is important.

9270 kJ
2220 kcal
per day

● **On task 2**

There are lots of leaflets about balanced diets. Some are written for supermarkets and food companies. Others are written by groups such as the Health Education Authority and the Department of Health.

1. Use the leaflets and information available to you. Investigate foods that make up a balanced diet. Make notes as you work. You will need to present your findings to Sunshine Stores on your design sheet.

2. Use Web sites on the Internet to find recipe ideas that provide balanced meals. For example:

   www.tesco.co.uk

   Write down some recipe ideas on your design sheet.

3. Read through **An Interview with M&S** on the next page. It will help you find out how food companies meet consumer demands for balanced products.

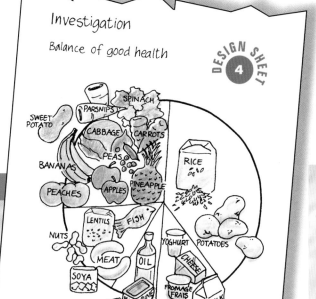

On your design sheet

- Write down how much energy you need in one day.

- Record your investigation using drawings, tables and graphs.

- Record some ideas for healthy recipes.

Remember

- Food energy is measured in kilojoules or kilocalories.

- Different people require different amounts of food energy.

- Everybody should have a varied diet.

5

MARKS & SPENCER

Marks and Spencer has a wide range of products showing healthy-eating symbols. The information here will help you design your new balanced cook–chill meal.

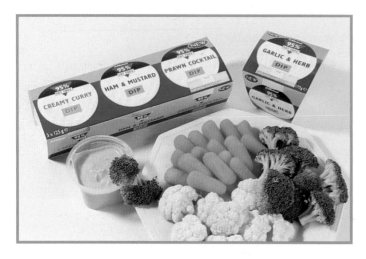

Why have you chosen to produce a healthy-eating range of products?

" Current healthy-eating advice suggests that we increase the amount of fresh fruit and vegetables that we eat and reduce our fat intake.

Customers now demand healthy foods so we've produced a range of products with a lowered level of fat.

We carefully select ingredients naturally low in fats and use modern processing techniques. "

How do consumers know your range is healthy-eating?

" We use a standard logo – a coloured, upside down, triangle. This indicates the product is part of our healthy-eating range.

A green triangle refers to low fat, reduced fat or a certain percentage fat-free.

A blue triangle indicates the product is below a certain number of calories.

We also include full nutritional information on the products. "

HALF FAT
Lite

NATURALLY
98%
FAT FREE

LESS THAN
300
CALS
PER ▼ PACK

Could you briefly describe the cook–chill process that you use?

❝ Products are cooked to a minimum of 75°C, at the coolest point; then they are rapidly chilled to below 5°C. ❞

Why do you think cook–chill products are so popular today?

❝ People's lifestyles mean they have less time to prepare meals. Consequently recipe dishes (such as cook–chill lasagne) provide an extremely convenient option to cooking. It means that in only a few minutes, a delicious meal can be served.

International travel has meant that customers have been introduced to wider styles of food. Recipe dishes mean customers do not have to keep a wide range of ingredients for preparing different meals.

Also, traditional cooking skills needed to make dishes of this standard are not as common today. ❞

What advice would you give someone designing a new, healthy and tasty cook–chill meal?

❝ Use all natural ingredients. Do not compromise on quality, texture and flavour – use the most suitable ingredients and methods available. ❞

On your design sheet

- Show how you might be able to use a logo or symbol like Marks and Spencer's to inform consumers about the ingredients in your new product.

Balancing Health

Everyone is being encouraged to lead a healthy lifestyle. A balanced diet should be part of that lifestyle. It is also important to enjoy your food – both eating and making!

Have you ever seen a potato masher like this?

Balanced diets

Look at the picture below. It shows the proportion of different foods in a balanced diet. A balanced meal should follow the same proportions. Foods have been put in those proportions because of the nutrients they contain (see pages 16 and 17).

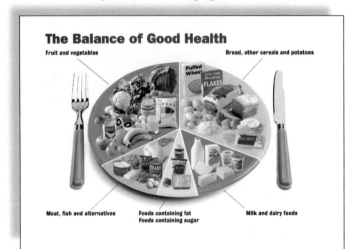

The Balance of Good Health

Fruit and vegetables

Bread, other cereals and potatoes

Meat, fish and alternatives

Foods containing fat
Foods containing sugar

Milk and dairy foods

This is a poster published by the Health Education Authority

Fruit and vegetables

I don't like vegetables! I don't eat fruit!

How many people say that? Yet there is a wide range of both fruit and vegetables. They all look and taste different. They add texture, flavour and colour to food products. They also provide vitamins, minerals and **NSP** (non-starch polysaccharide, or dietary fibre). This helps waste products leave the body quickly and easily, preventing constipation.

Bread, cereals and potatoes

These foods have been put together in one group. They should make up a large proportion of the daily diet. They all provide the carbohydrate starch. They also contain other nutrients. On their own these foods are low in fat. They provide NSP, especially wholemeal breads and cereals.

Vitamins and minerals

44

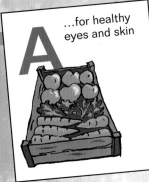
...for healthy eyes and skin

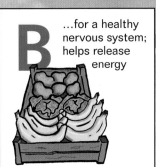
...for a healthy nervous system; helps release energy

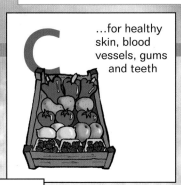
...for healthy skin, blood vessels, gums and teeth

Each vitamin and mineral plays an important role in the body. They are needed in small amounts every day. On the right are a few examples.

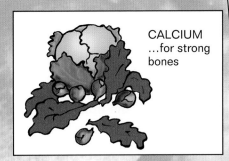
CALCIUM ...for strong bones

POTASSIUM ...for healthy muscles and nerves

MAGNESIUM ...for healthy cells and enzyme functions; works with calcium

IRON ...in the blood helps to carry oxygen from the lungs to the tissues

● On task 1

Salt is often added to potatoes and rice during cooking. It helps bring out the flavour of food. Too much salt in the diet is thought to be unhealthy for some people.

Carry out an investigation to see whether potatoes can be flavoured with other ingredients. Make notes during your investigation. Record the results on design sheet **6a**.

● On task 2

1. Think about different potato dishes. Look through recipes in magazines, books, software and on the Internet. You may discover recipes like hot pot, fishcakes, vegetable curry and cottage pie.

2. Choose three ideas for potato dishes. How could you make them suitable for Sunshine Stores?

3. Record your ideas by writing down the ingredients with quantities on design sheet **6b**. Use sketches if you wish.

6a

Flavouring	Description of taste and appearance
Control	The potato tasted very bland. It had a creamy colour and did not look very appetising
Salt	The taste was like ordinary potato; it did not have much flavour. It was cream coloured.
Parsley	This potato had a strong herby flavour. It was speckled with green and looked unusual but quite attractive.

On your design sheets

● Make notes about your potato investigation. **6a**

● Write the results from your investigation. **6a**

● Record three ideas for potato dishes. **6b**

Remember

● A balanced diet should contain a high proportion of carbohydrate (starch).

● A balanced diet contains lots of fruit and vegetables.

● Each vitamin and mineral has an important role in the body.

7

Tried and Tested

Designing with food involves testing ideas. This means making the food product and tasting it. Sight, hearing, touch and sense of smell are needed too!

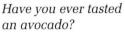

Have you ever tasted an avocado?

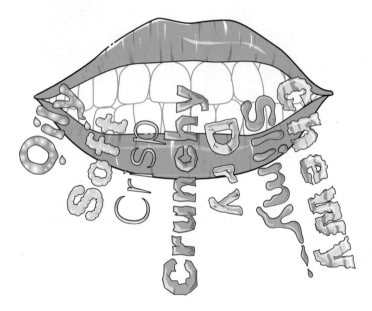

Feeling tasty

We often use our hands to eat and prepare food. A cake that feels hard and dry will probably taste stale. If an avocado can be pressed with the thumb it is likely to be ripe. Once in the mouth we can feel the texture of the food. This is known as **mouthfeel**.

Smelling tasty

The smell of a food is known as **aroma**. The aroma of baking bread or frying bacon can make us feel hungry. When we eat our sense of smell and taste work together. Sometimes we cannot detect flavours very clearly. This might be because a blocked nose stops the sense of smell.

Looking tasty

Imagine being given a completely new food to eat. You have no idea how it might taste. But you can look at it. If it looks tasty you might be tempted to try it. If consumers buy a new cook–chill product they want to know it will not be wasted, so looking tasty is important.

Sounding tasty

Of course products in a chill cabinet do not usually make a noise! But we often use our hearing when it comes to food. What about that noisy breakfast cereal – snap, crackle and pop? Listening to food being chopped or fried can make you feel hungry. It can make your mouth water as it fills with saliva.

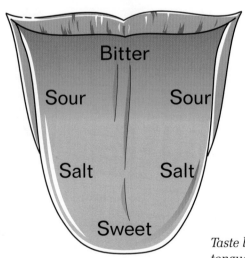

Taste buds on our tongue help us to taste different flavours

Sensory tests

Testing design ideas involves consumers in the target group. They taste the product and record what they think. They may be asked about certain qualities. For example, they may be asked about its colour. They could give the meal a mark out of five for its golden brown colour. These are **sensory qualities**.

For your testing you may have to use your family and friends.

● On task

1. Choose one of your three potato dish ideas to test. You may wish to record it again with more detail. On your design sheet, say why you have chosen it.

2. List four qualities you would like your product to have. These can be to do with looks, sound, smell, taste or feel. Look at the example on the left. It has been drawn as a star profile.

3. Draw a star profile for your design idea. Add your four sensory qualities.

4. Make your product.

5. Ask two or three people to evaluate your product and complete the star profile. Use a different colour pen for each taster.

DESIGN SHEET 7

The design idea I chose for my potato dish was a Potato and Cheese Layer. I chose this idea because I thought the cheesy flavour would be good with potatoes which are quite bland. I also thought it would suit my target consumer group: teenagers. They can easily reheat it and would enjoy the creamy and soft textures.

Star profile: cheesy flavour, smooth sauce, golden brown on top, creamy texture (scale 1–5)

Next time I will grill the top for longer. This will make it more golden in colour.

On your design sheet

- Explain which potato dish you have chosen and why.

- Draw a star profile with four sensory qualities.

- Present the results of two or three sensory evaluations.

Remember

- Testing food involves using all five senses.

- Mouthfeel is the texture of food in our mouths.

- Aroma is the smell of food.

- Star profiles are a quick way to show sensory test results.

Pack, Heat and Eat

8

A QUESTION of Balance

Cook–chill meals are very convenient. Consumers just heat them and eat them! But this could not happen without the right type of packaging and storage.

Recycling symbols can be seen on many types of packaging

Packaging materials

The type of packaging chosen for food products is very important. It must keep the food (or drink) fresh. It must protect the food. Cook–chill packaging must withstand very cold and very hot temperatures. It usually uses both plastic and card materials.

Card packaging

Cardboard is made from woodpulp. It can be printed, waxed, glazed and strengthened. Below are some examples of the uses of cardboard.

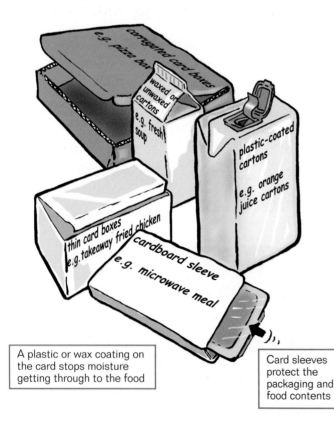

corrugated card boxes e.g. pizza box

waxed or unwaxed cartons e.g. fresh soup

plastic-coated cartons e.g. orange juice cartons

thin card boxes e.g. takeaway fried chicken

cardboard sleeve e.g. microwave meal

A plastic or wax coating on the card stops moisture getting through to the food

Card sleeves protect the packaging and food contents

Plastic packaging

Most food packaging is thermo-plastic. This means the plastic becomes soft when it is heated. It can then be shaped or moulded. When the plastic cools it sets hard.

PP (polypropylene)
- can be moulded into containers
- can withstand high and low temperatures
- can be used as plastic film

PET (polyester)
- can be used as a film
- can be moulded into containers
- can withstand very high temperatures

PVC (polyvinylchloride)
- can be flexible
- can withstand high and low temperatures

PS (polystyrene)
- can cushion or protect food
- can keep food hot (insulate)

● On task 1

On design sheet **8a**:

1. Draw or describe the material(s) you would choose for packaging the following food items:

► bottle of fizzy drink

► microwave meal

► take-away chicken in a bun

► some leftover fruit salad in the fridge at home

► apple juice

► chocolate mousse

► take-away pizza.

Give reasons for your choices where possible.

2. Draw or describe the packaging for your new cook–chill meal. Include the materials you would use.

New cook-chill meal

DESIGN SHEET 8a

NEW
Balanced Meals Range

JAMBALAYA

MADE WITH BASMATI RICE, CHICKEN, ONION, PEPPERS, CELERY, TOMATOES

Reheating instructions:
Oven type: Microwave
Category D
Temperature: High (100%)
Time 1½ mins

PP
(Polypropylene)

I have chosen to develop a rice dish because my target group is teenagers. In my survey the teenagers said they preferred rice to potatoes.

Heat it up

The containers used for cook–chill meals can withstand very high temperatures. The meals must be reheated to make them safe to eat. This is usually done in the oven or microwave.

Probing the centre

A food probe is used in industry. It measures the temperature at the centre of the food. Food being reheated must reach a temperature of 72°C in the middle. A probe ensures food is cooked (or frozen) right the way through.

● On task 2

On design sheet **8b**:

1. Decide whether your cook–chill meal will contain rice or potatoes. Explain why you made this choice.

2. Choose another design idea to test.

3. Make your design idea.

4. Cool quickly, wrap and chill in the fridge.

5. When you are ready to reheat your meal, make a note of the following:

► type of oven

► temperature/setting

► time taken.

On your design sheets

● Record the answers to your packaging investigation. **8a**

● Record your choice of rice or potato dish, with reasons. **8b**

● Write down the reheating instructions for your cook–chill product. **8b**

Remember

● Packaging can protect food.

● Packaging can help to keep food fresh.

● Plastic can be moulded to make different types and shapes of packaging.

● Packaging should be recycled wherever possible.

Perfect Planning

9

Working with food always involves planning, from what to have for dinner to producing hundreds of meals in one day!

Planning for production

Step one

Perfect planning must start at the beginning. To make your final design idea, you need to know the ingredients. The ingredients must be in good condition. This means you have the makings of a perfect product.

Step two

Your final design will have a recipe. This will list the quantities you need. Weigh and measure the ingredients accurately. Scales should be checked to make sure they are working properly.

Step three

Tools and equipment will be needed during the production. Choose the most suitable equipment. This may involve trying various types to find the best one.

Step four

Find the most convenient order for making the product: This means choosing the job to be done first. Then the second, and so on. This requires careful planning.

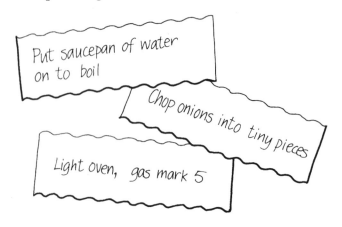

Put saucepan of water on to boil

Chop onions into tiny pieces

Light oven, gas mark 5

● On task 1

1. List the ingredients for your rice or potato dish on your design sheet.

2. List or draw the equipment needed.

3. On rough paper, list the steps for making your product. Leave a gap between each one. Number them on the back. Cut out the steps.

4. Muddle up the steps. Ask a friend to put them in the order they would follow. Did they choose the same order? Were any steps missing?

5. Add any missing instructions then re-number your method if necessary. This can be done on the front of the pieces of paper.

6. Stick down or rewrite the steps in the right order.

Healthy checks

A perfect product must be made safely and hygienically. Checks need to be carried out during production. These must be added to production plans. Health and safety checks may include:

▷ hygiene rules being followed by people working with food
▷ use-by and best-before dates for all ingredients
▷ storage of ingredients and food products
▷ clean equipment and work surfaces before and after production
▷ temperature of oven/fridge.

Quality checks

Sunshine Stores require a perfect product. This means using quality checks throughout the production. These checks may include:

▷ correct weighing/measuring of ingredients
▷ correct size of tins/dishes
▷ correct portion sizes
▷ taste testing during production (hygienically)
▷ visual check of a product's appearance.

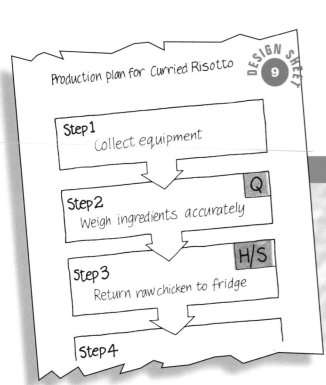

Production plan for Curried Risotto

DESIGN SHEET 9

Step 1 Collect equipment

Step 2 Weigh ingredients accurately Q

Step 3 Return raw chicken to fridge H/S

Step 4

PRODUCTION PLAN
for Cheese and Tomato Potato Layer

H/S =	Health and safety check
Q =	Quality check

Step one

Wash hands, tie back hair, put on apron.	H/S
Clean work surface. Collect and check equipment.	H/S

Step two

Weigh all ingredients.	Q

Step three

Peel and wash potatoes. Cut into pieces using chopping board and sharp knife.	

Step four

Sizes must be equal.	Q

● On task 2

What health and safety checks and quality checks will your product need?

1. Look at your production steps again.

2. Use a coloured pen to add health and safety checks.

3. Use a different colour to add quality checks.

4. If there is time, test your production plan by making your final product. Follow your plan and note any changes needed.

5. Write out your final production plan with all necessary checks on your design sheet.

On your design sheet

● List all ingredients needed.

● List all equipment and tools needed.

● Present your production plan as a flow chart. Include health and safety checks and quality checks.

Remember

● Successful food products need careful planning.

● Planning includes health and safety checks and quality checks.

Success on a Plate

Now it is time for you to evaluate your success. What will Sunshine Stores think of your healthy meal-for-one?

Specific points

Sunshine Stores asked you to design and make a meal. It set out guidelines for the meal:

SUNSHINE STORES
New Product Specification

The product must:

- be a main meal ❏
- contain rice or potato ❏
- contain a balance of ingredients ❏
- be sold from the chill cabinet ❏

This is the **specification** for the new product.

How well does your meal match it?

Sensory testing

You will need to use your senses to evaluate your product. You will also need to ask others what they think. This could be done using a star profile. Or you may prefer to use a tasting chart.

Product name: Spicy Potato Curry				
	Taster 1	Taster 2	Taster 3	Taster 4
Appearance	lovely golden colour	looks very appetising	Looks tasty and colourful	golden brown sauce w colourful
Aroma	spicy but not overpowering	spicy aroma	Quite spicy and garlicky	not too strong or spicy
Texture	a mixture of smooth and crunchy	Sauce is smooth, vegetables crunchy	Potatoes are soft, other veg have got a bite	good balance soft crunchy
Taste	Rice creamy and spicy	Just the right amount of spice	delicious! spicy and creamy	very tasty: lots of different flavours

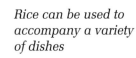

Rice can be used to accompany a variety of dishes

Target group

All new products must suit their consumers. Who did you design your meal for? You need to find out if they like the taste. Your product must also match the consumer's needs. This means thinking about:

▷ portion size (e.g. enough kJ/kcal for a growing teenager)
▷ acceptable ingredients (e.g. completely vegetarian items)
▷ appealing looks (e.g. shaped like a dinosaur to please a toddler)
▷ cost (e.g. selling price is similar to other cook–chill meals)
▷ suitable instructions (e.g. includes cooker as well as microwave)

Even better

Sometimes even a final design can be improved. Perhaps the method needs altering, or an ingredient needs to be changed. Any improvements can make your final product even better next time you make it. It is during the evaluation these changes can be suggested.

● On task

1. On your design sheet, tick each point in the specification matched by your meal. Can you think of any other points to add to the list? For example, is it suitable for vegetarians?

2. Make your final cook–chill meal. Carry out a sensory test. If possible, use your consumer target group. Record the results on your design sheet.

3. Note any changes that would make your meal even better. Try to say why the changes are needed.

On your design sheet

● Tick the specification list you have made.
● Present your sensory testing results.
● Note any changes that may be needed.

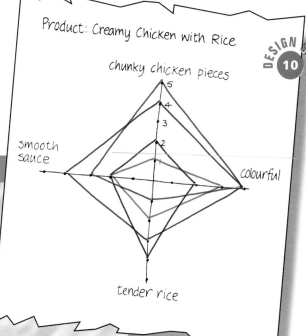

Product: Creamy Chicken with Rice

chunky chicken pieces

smooth sauce

colourful

tender rice

DESIGN SHEET 10

Remember

● A final product must match its specification.
● Sensory tests are used to evaluate products.
● A final product must suit its target consumer group.

Starting Point

3 GET the IDEA?

Food technologists come up with new ideas for food products all the time. Where do they get their ideas from? How do manufacturers know how to make them?

Maltbys is a food manufacturer. The company has asked you to design a new flavoured bread product. It could be sweet or savoury.

A rival manufacturer is just about to launch a new bread snack. Maltbys want to provide some competition.

Can you design and make an exciting new bread product?

The challenge

Maltbys have not suggested a target consumer group. Your challenge is to find a 'gap' in the market. You have to design something that consumers cannot buy at the moment.

Same product,
New Idea

Making Bread Rise

3 — 4 — 5

Making Bread

8 — 7 — 6

Selling a New Idea Modifying Genes An Interview with...
Allied Bakeries

The focus

There are many bread products on sale already.
You need to discover what consumers think of
them. Also find out why consumers do not buy
bread products! To make a successful product
you must find out how different breads are made.

The end product

Maltbys want a new product that will beat its
rivals! Your product must be carefully tested and
evaluated.

Maltbys need to know that you understand why
you have used certain ingredients. The correct
method is essential too. Make sure you use
information you have learnt about ingredients and
methods.

Are you up to the
challenge?

Different Doughs

There are many bread products on the market today. They come in a variety of flavours, shapes and sizes. Consumers can serve them at breakfast time, as a snack or to accompany a meal.

Here you will investigate what products are already available.

Versatile bread

A basic bread dough made with yeast can be used to make a variety of products. The flavoured bread products shown below include loaves made with different types of flour, pizza bases, rolls, baps, cobs and buns.

Cultural influence

The British diet is influenced by foods from other cultures. Bread is no exception. We live in a **multicultural** society and we are lucky enough to experience breads from other countries such as Indian naan bread, Mexican cornbread, French pain au chocolat, Italian ciabatta and Austrian stollen.

Testing and tasting

Before food technologists begin to design new food products they often look at the existing market. This means they evaluate the products already available.

The evaluation will involve looking at the appearance, cost and packaging of the product. There will also be a tasting session to evaluate the products' appearance, texture, aroma and taste. This is known as sensory analysis. Descriptive words are carefully chosen to match the food's taste, texture, aroma and appearance.

Taste	nutty	
Texture	doughy	
Aroma	yeasty	

Sensory descriptors for bread

● *On task*

1. Working in groups, complete the table at the top of your design sheet. List five words that you might use to describe the taste of any bread product. Then list five words for its aroma and five words for texture.

As a class, share your words and produce a 'tasting sheet' containing all your sensory descriptors.

2. Evaluate the bread products provided by your teacher. Use your descriptive words to help you. Complete the product evaluation table on your design sheet.

3. Working with a partner, look at your results table. How will the information help you when designing? Think about:

► a new look
► a different flavour
► the type of texture.

Production evaluation	Product 1	Product 2
Name		
Description of packaging		
Cost		
Weight		
Appearance		
Taste		
Texture		
Aroma		

Comparing existing bread products

Today I compared five different bread products.

Three were savoury and two were sweet. This investigation will help me design a new bread product because:

• none of the products were very colourful. I could design something containing ingredients like dried apricots, cherries or nuts to make it look interesting.

DESIGN SHEET 1

On your design sheet

● Record your sensory descriptors. Add to them during the project if you can.

● Complete the table showing your bread comparisons.

● Explain how this information can help when designing a new bread product.

Remember

● Bread is a very versatile food product.

● The British diet is influenced by many other cultures.

● Food technologists often evaluate existing products before designing a new one.

Talking to Consumers

2 GET the IDEA?

When designing new food products it is important to find out what consumers want. A consumer survey can help you find a gap in the market.

Consumer survey

Food technologists must ask consumers for their opinions. A questionnaire is a straightforward way to gather information from a range of people.

The purpose

What is the purpose of your questionnaire? When designing a new flavoured bread product the purpose might be to find out:

▷ who eats flavoured bread products?
▷ what type do they eat?
▷ what new products might they enjoy?

Remind yourself about questionnaires by looking back to pages 38–9.

Suitable questions

A questionnaire should contain a series of clear questions. Most should be **closed** questions with specific answers. **Open-ended** questions are usually put at the end of the questionnaire. They provide the food technologist with extra information written by the consumer.

Examples of some suitable closed questions might be:

Do you regularly eat flavoured bread products (e.g. three times a week or more)

Yes ☐
No ☐

Which of the following have you eaten in the last 2 weeks? Tick all that apply.

Ciabatta ☐
Chelsea bun ☐
Cheese-topped baps ☐
Sesame breadsticks ☐
Frenchbread pizza ☐
Fruit buns

Other .... ☐

None

Target group

Sometimes food technologists have to find a suitable consumer 'target group' for their new product. This means the product may be aimed at groups such as children, older people, working adults, the health conscious or those on a special diet.

It is useful to find out which group people belong to when carrying out a survey. For example, research might show that very few young children choose products containing cheese. Or, the majority of older people prefer individual products like rolls rather than loaves of bread.

Finding out people's consumer group and their dietary needs could be done like this:

New ideas

To discover what consumers want, a questionnaire might contain an open-ended question. The final question could be something like this:

> On what occasions do you buy flavoured bread products?
>
> We always used to buy a sticky bun to eat after shopping on Saturdays. I'm trying to loose weight, so we don't do that now. I really miss them though!

● **On task**

1. On design sheet **2a**, prepare a questionnaire to help you find out:

   ▶ who eats flavoured bread products
   ▶ what type they choose to eat
   ▶ what new products they might like to try.

   Use the information on these pages to help you.

   When your questions have been checked, word-process your questionnaire if possible.

2. Carry out your survey. Ask at least five people.

3. When you have gathered your results, decide on a suitable consumer target group. Explain on design sheet **2b** why they have been chosen.

4. Present your survey results on design sheet **2b**. Use bar charts and graphs if possible.

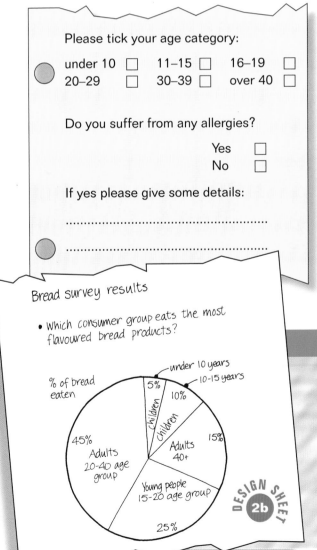

Please tick your age category:

under 10 ☐   11–15 ☐   16–19 ☐
20–29 ☐   30–39 ☐   over 40 ☐

Do you suffer from any allergies?

Yes ☐
No ☐

If yes please give some details:

....

....

Bread survey results

• Which consumer group eats the most flavoured bread products?

% of bread eaten

under 10 years — 5%
10-15 years — 10%
Children
Children — 15%
Adults 40+
45% Adults 20-40 age group
Young people 15-20 age group
25%

DESIGN SHEET 2b

On your design sheets

● Present your consumer questionnaire. **2a**

● Explain who will be your target consumer group and why. **2b**

● Present the results from your survey using bar charts and graphs. **2b**

Remember

● Before designing new products it is important to find out what consumers want.

● A questionnaire is a convenient way to identify a target consumer group.

Same Product, New Idea

3

GET the IDEA?

There has been a recent twist in new product development. Existing products have been turned into new ones without even changing the name!

If it works, don't change it

Some food products on our supermarket shelves today have been around for years. To many they are household names, like Kellogg's Cornflakes, Mars Bars and Rowntree's Jelly.

The latest fashion in food technology is to transform a household name into a trendy new product. A Mars Bar is a chocolate bar but now it also exists as a Mars Ice Cream Bar – same product, new idea!

Other products to follow the trend are shown here.

Kellogg's Rice Krispies	➔ Kellogg's Rice Crispies breakfast cereal chewy marshmallow Squares
Cadbury's Caramel bar	➔ Cadbury's Caramel Cakes
Milky Way chocolate	➔ Milky Way Crispy Rolls
McVities Digestive biscuits	➔ Mini Digestive biscuits on top of Yoplait yoghurt
Heinz Baked Beans	➔ Heinz Baked Bean Pizza
Bagels	➔ Microwave Bagel Bites with cheese and tomatoes

We have the technology

Designing a new product from an existing one does not mean the process is any easier.

Food technologists may need to change existing ingredients quite a lot to ensure the product will work. A Mars Ice Cream Bar is not just a Mars Bar that has been frozen!

At the same time, the end result must be acceptable to the consumer. Kellogg's Rice Krispie Squares, for example, must have the appearance, flavour and texture of the original Rice Krispies.

On task 1

1. Choose one of the bread recipes provided by your teacher. They do not require yeast, so they are quick and easy. Make the bread as it is or add extra flavouring ingredients.

2. When you have made your bread describe your results on design sheet **3a**.

3. Write down on your design sheet one thing you learnt when making your bread. For example, 'I did not know sweetcorn came from maize and that it could be used to make bread'.

On task 2

Begin to think about new bread products. Your ideas could be as imaginative as you like at this stage. Record six design ideas for your project on design sheet **3b**. Remember you are designing a flavoured bread product. Think about these points:

► sweet or savoury?

► individual or whole product?

► shape?

► glaze/finish/topping?

► target consumer group?

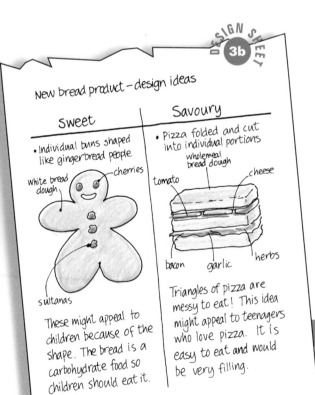

DESIGN SHEET 3b

New bread product – design ideas

Sweet	Savoury
• Individual buns shaped like gingerbread people	• Pizza folded and cut into individual portions

white bread dough — cherries

sultanas

These might appeal to children because of the shape. The bread is a carbohydrate food so children should eat it.

wholemeal bread dough

tomato — cheese

bacon   garlic   herbs

Triangles of pizza are messy to eat! This idea might appeal to teenagers who love pizza. It is easy to eat and would be very filling.

On your design sheets

● Record your results for an easy bread, including what you have learnt. **3a**

● Present six design ideas for your flavoured bread product. **3b**

Remember

● There is a current trend in designing new products from existing ones.

● Bread products can be made using a wide range of ingredients.

Making Bread

Bread is a very useful product for the consumer. It is useful for the food technologist, too.

The flavour, shape, texture, size and ingredients can all be altered to make an endless variety of new ideas.

Choice of ingredients

In order to investigate the production of bread, a basic dough made with yeast will be studied. The main ingredients are:

Flour
Strong (bread) flour is usually chosen for breadmaking.

Fat
By adding a small amount of fat (butter, oil, or margarine) the texture of the bread can be improved. A moist bread does not stale so quickly.

Salt
A little salt can give flavour to the dough.

Sugar
Sugar is not essential. It is often added to sweet bread mixtures.

Liquid
Water, milk or a mixture of both may be used. Milk helps to give a soft texture and brown crust. It is difficult to know precisely how much liquid is needed. This is because flours absorb liquids differently. However, the liquid must be warm or tepid (37°C) for the yeast to work properly.

Yeast
Yeast makes the bread rise; it is the **raising agent**. You will learn more about raising agents on pages 64–5.

Fresh yeast can be bought from some bakers and supermarkets. It is quick and easy to use, although it must be blended with warm liquid first.

Dried yeast is a concentrated form of fresh yeast. Like all dried foods, it keeps well. It needs to be mixed with warm liquid and left to stand before being used.

Easyblend yeast is also in dried form but can be used straight-way by mixing it with the flour.

● On task

When designing a new bread product you will need to decide which type of yeast to use. Investigate different yeasts by working in groups of three.

▶ person 1 uses fresh yeast

▶ person 2 uses dried yeast

▶ person 3 uses easyblend yeast.

1. Prepare a batch of bread rolls following your teacher's instructions.

2. Make notes while you are working. Record information which will help you complete the table on your design sheet (see below).

3. When you are ready to evaluate the results, you will each need one of your bread rolls.

▶ Explain how you used the yeast.

▶ Weigh each roll.

▶ Cut each roll in half and measure the height.

▶ Describe the roll's appearance.

▶ Describe the roll's texture.

▶ Describe the roll's taste.

4. Write your conclusions at the bottom of your design sheet. Which yeast will you chose and why? If you are not using yeast in your bread product, explain why.

	Bread 1	Bread 2
Type of yeast used		
How yeast was used		
Weight of one roll		
Height of roll		
Appearance		
Taste		
Texture		
Aroma		

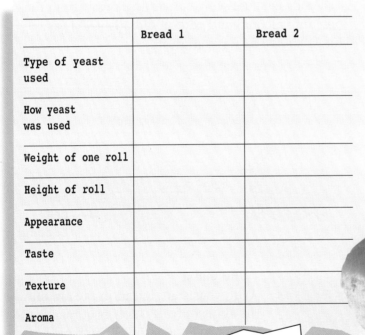

After investigating different types of yeast I have decided I will use easyblend yeast for my new bread product. It is quick and convenient. Also, my results showed the texture of that bread was better than the others.

DESIGN SHEET 4

On your design sheet

● Record the results of your yeast investigation.

● Explain which type of yeast (if any) you will choose for your bread product.

Remember

● Yeast is the raising agent used in many types of bread.

● Fresh, dried and easyblend yeasts are available.

Making Bread Rise

Making bread can be great fun – kneading the dough is a good way to get rid of excess energy! But how does that stretchy, elastic pale-looking dough become a tasty, open-textured loaf of bread?

Raising agents

Many food products contain raising agents. A raising agent is something that makes the food rise and become light in texture. Raising agents are used in products such as cakes, desserts, breads, Yorkshire puddings, scones, muffins and pastries. All raising agents are **gases**. They may be:

▷ gas incorporated while making the product; for example, the liquid in muffins creates *steam*, whisking a Swiss roll mixture adds air

▷ something added to the product which will produce a gas; for example, baking powder added to some cakes, self-raising flour used in scones, yeast for breadmaking. These give off carbon dioxide which makes the product rise.

Many products use a combination of raising agents.

Yeast

Yeast is a living organism. It can multiply continually if it is given the right conditions. Yeast needs *warmth, food, moisture and time*. When making bread the yeast has flour for its 'food', liquid for its moisture and it is left in a warm place – ideal conditions for yeast!

Fermentation

Yeast multiplies by separating off part of its cell to form a bud. The bud grows and becomes a separate yeast cell which, in turn, forms another bud, and so on. These cells are minute and can only be seen under a microscope. During this **budding** process, yeast cells get energy by converting sugar (from the flour) into alcohol and carbon dioxide (CO_2) gas. This is known as **fermentation**.

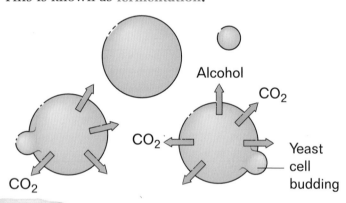

Alcohol

CO_2

CO_2

CO_2

CO_2

Yeast cell budding

Wild yeast

Wild yeasts are found in the air, on the skins of fruit (such as grapes) and in the husks of grain. They have been used for thousands of years to ferment beer and make bread.

The bread process

Fermentation takes place at different stages of the breadmaking process.

1. Liquid, warmth, time and food are needed for yeast to multiply.

2. The starch in flour is broken down by an enzyme to form sugar (maltose).

3. Yeast ferments with the sugar to produce carbon dioxide and alcohol.

4. The carbon dioxide acts as a raising agent: it makes the dough rise when left in a warm place.

5. During baking the dough continues to rise until the yeast is killed by the high temperature. The bread **sets** in its risen state.

● On task 1

Find out more about how bread is made industrially by reading the interview with Allied Bakeries on the next page.

● On task 2

1. Choose one of your six design ideas to test. You will need to think very carefully about each ingredient and the method.

2. Describe or sketch the idea in detail on design sheet **5a**. List the ingredients and quantities.

3. Prepare a star profile on design sheet **5b** ready for your evaluation. Decide which sensory qualities you would like your product to have (such as golden brown colour, soft texture).

4. Make and evaluate your design idea. Ask friends and family to help you evaluate the sensory qualities. If possible, use people from your consumer target group.

5. Describe improvements you could now make to your design ideas.

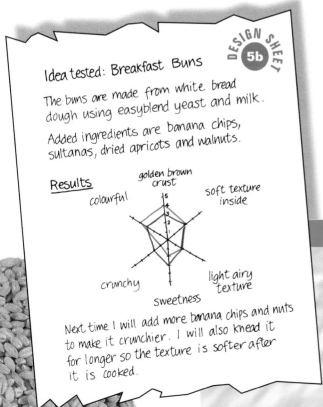

DESIGN SHEET 5b

Idea tested: Breakfast Buns

The buns are made from white bread dough using easyblend yeast and milk.
Added ingredients are banana chips, sultanas, dried apricots and walnuts.

Results

golden brown crust
soft texture inside
colourful
light airy texture
crunchy
sweetness

Next time I will add more banana chips and nuts to make it crunchier. I will also knead it for longer so the texture is softer after it is cooked.

On your design sheets

- Record your chosen design in detail. **5a**

- Evaluate your results using a star profile. **5b**

- Suggest any improvements to your ideas. **5b**

Remember

- Many food products need a raising agent to make them rise.

- Yeast is a living organism which can multiply continually, given the right conditions.

- Yeast needs warmth, time, moisture and food in order to multiply.

- During fermentation yeast gives off carbon dioxide and alcohol.

An Interview with...

6 GET the IDEA?

Allied Bakeries produce a variety of breads and bread products using different brand names. Here you can see how their products are made.

ALLIED BAKERIES

What type of savoury bread products do you produce?

" Allied Bakeries produce a wide range of different breads and bread products. Some of our more unusual varieties include soya and linseed bread, Sunmalt malt loaf, wholemeal pitta and croissants. "

Which method of bread production do you use?

" A lot of our bread production uses the Chorleywood Breadmaking Process (CBP) which is shown here:

1. Ingredients mixed in a high speed mixer to produce a dough. 	2. Dividing and moulding of the dough into weighed pieces. 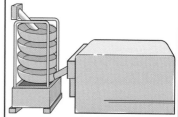
3. Initial short proof period. 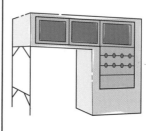	4. Remoulding of the dough and placing into tins. 
5. Second proof of about 50 minutes. 	6. Baking. 7. Cooling. 8. Slicing (if required) and packaging. 9. Despatch and distribution. 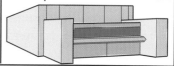

How would you go about launching a new bread product?

❝ We will make sure there is a market for the product by collecting detailed information from consumers. When we launch the product we may use introductory offers, money-off coupons and advertising on television, posters, in magazines, on tubes or buses. ❞

On your design sheet

- Show how your new bread product might be made using the Chorleywood Breadmaking Process. Present the stages as a flow chart.

What do you need to consider when designing the packaging for your new product?

❝ All design work is carried out by design studios which we employ on a freelance basis to carry out design projects. We would normally brief the designer on:

▷ the type of project
▷ the position of the product in the market place (for example, is it for children?)
▷ the materials the packaging will be made from
▷ the printing process to be used
▷ how many colours are to be used
▷ what competitive products are on the market. ❞

What advice would you give someone designing and making a new flavoured bread product?

❝ I would advise them to look very carefully at the product market and identify a **gap** in that market. A gap is an area of the market where consumers' needs are not being met. Anybody can come up with a good idea but it must be one that consumers will want! ❞

Modifying Genes

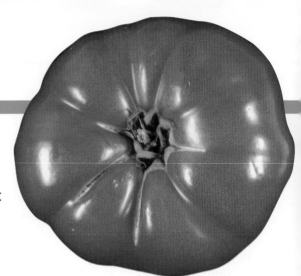

New ideas occur in food production all the time. Genetic modification is a recent development. How does it affect food products?

In the genes

Genes are strings of complex molecules found in every cell of all plants and animals. These genes carry the information needed by the cell to develop, grow and multiply. Genes are passed on from generation to generation.

Now scientists are learning to identify genes. They are finding out which gene controls which characteristic, for example, colour. They are also learning how to move or **transplant** genes from one plant or animal to another. This is called **genetic engineering** or **genetic modification**.

Splicing a gene

In food production, genes can be altered in two ways:

▷ by putting an end to a gene that causes an unwanted effect, such as tomatoes losing their firmness quickly
▷ by making a copy of a desirable gene and putting that copy into another plant or animal. This is known as **splicing** a gene.

Why bother?

Genetic modification is believed to benefit consumers and help the country's economy. The benefits include:

▷ genetically modified foods can be made to provide a higher nutritional value, for example adding more protein to rice
▷ plant crops may have a longer shelf-life and be more resistant to pests
▷ animals may be made more resistant to disease and grow faster
▷ food manufacture may be helped, as in genetically modified baker's yeast which improves the rising of bread dough.

Is it safe?

There is a lot of concern about genetic modification. Some people fear it could harm people or the environment. Take, for example, a crop modified to resist a herbicide. If the herbicide kills weeds only, could the crop and weeds together produce a 'superweed' which cannot be controlled?

There is also concern about unknown health risks from genetically modified ingredients in the diet.

Food technologists must keep up to date with any new food developments. However, at the moment in the UK, genetically modified foods are being grown for trial but not for sale.

Labelling

The Government has set up controls to protect consumers, animals, the environment and those who work in genetic modification research.

From 1st September 1998, it has been a legal requirement to label foods containing genetically modified soya or maize ingredients.

Many shops and fast food chains have banned all genetically modified foods and ingredients from their own-label products until more is known about their effects.

The Great Engineered British Breakfast – scientists are exploring genetic modifications to all of the food products on this plate

● On task 1

If any of the ingredients in your product (e.g. tomato puree) could be genetically engineered, how might this benefit the consumer and/or the manufacturer?

DESIGN SHEET 7a

Design idea: Orange and Cinnamon Buns

sticky tops   golden colour

400g strong flour
7g sachet dried easyblend yeast
50g margarine
50g muscovado sugar
200ml milk
10ml cinnamon
grated rind of 1 orange
1 egg

light, open texture   Makes 9 buns

glazed with orange juice and sugar

● On task 2

Next you need to modify your design ideas (not your genes!) Look back at your design ideas again. Choose a different idea to test.

1. Describe or sketch the idea in detail on design sheet **7a**. List all the ingredients with quantities.

2. How will you make this product? Record the method, step by step, on design sheet **7b**. A flow chart is a useful way to do this.

3. Make your product following your production plan.

4. How could your production plan be improved? Did you use the right equipment? Could you have shaped your product(s) more accurately? Was the baking time correct? Record this evaluation on design sheet **7b**.

On your design sheets

● Record in detail the design idea you are going to test. **7a**

● Produce a production plan. **7b**

● Evaluate your results. Write down how your idea could be improved. **7b**

Remember

● Genetically modified foods have had their genes changed in some way.

● There is still a lot of concern about genetically modified foods.

Selling a New Idea

A great deal of time, effort and money goes into the development of a new product. For that product to be a success, the food company producing it must work just as hard on its presentation.

Image

Presentation is not just about packaging. Of course, the design of packaging is very important. A new product must catch the consumer's eye. It must be user-friendly. This means it must show clearly what the product is and how it can be used or served, and it must be easy to open.

A new product needs to have an **image**. This image is one that will appeal to the target consumer group. The image can be presented on the packaging and in advertisements and promotional material. Examples of images that might be presented include:

▷ healthy and nutritious
▷ traditional and reliable
▷ young and trendy
▷ convenient and uncomplicated
▷ luxurious and extravagant
▷ superior and good quality
▷ economical.

Target groups

Food products like sweets are often aimed at children. They are more likely to have brightly coloured cartoon characters on their packaging. Their labels probably won't mention nutritional value! However, the nutrients in a children's meal or dessert may be highlighted because an adult is likely to choose this type of product.

A great deal of research goes into the image of a product. Sometimes food products are advertised using people who could belong to the target group. This way consumers can identify with the product and may therefore wish to buy it.

● On task

1. Think about your consumer target group and consider its needs. What sort of images might appeal to people? On design sheet **8a**, present an image for your new product by either:

   ▶ describing its packaging, or
   ▶ sketching and labelling its packaging.

   You should convey a clear message about your product's image. This may be done through colour, lettering, the product's name, pictures, special features (nutritional, healthy eating, easy to open, etc.)

2. You have tested two of your design ideas. Which idea will be your final product? Describe your final idea on design sheet **8b**. Say why you have chosen it. How does it meet the consumer group's needs?

3. Make your final product. Evaluate it on design sheet **8c**. Use a star profile or a taste testing table (see page 37).

4. Finally, you need to produce a report to send to Maltbys. If possible, use a word processor. Use words and sketches to show:

   ▶ that your final product matches Maltby's task

   ▶ whether or not your product turned out as you intended

   ▶ whether you chose an appropriate target consumer group

   ▶ what (if anything) you would alter to improve your product

   ▶ which parts of the project you feel show your best work.

   Give reasons for all your answers.

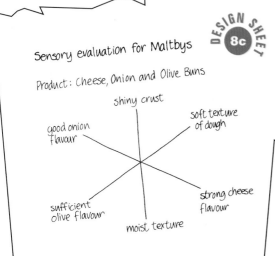

Sensory evaluation for Maltbys

Product: Cheese, Onion and Olive Buns

shiny crust
soft texture of dough
good onion flavour
strong cheese flavour
sufficient olive flavour
moist texture

DESIGN SHEET 8c

On your design sheets

- Describe or sketch the image you wish to present on your packaging. **8a**

- Present your final design idea and say why you have chosen it. **8b**

- Produce an evaluation of your final product as a star diagram or tasting table. **8c**

- Produce a short report on the production of your final product. **8c**

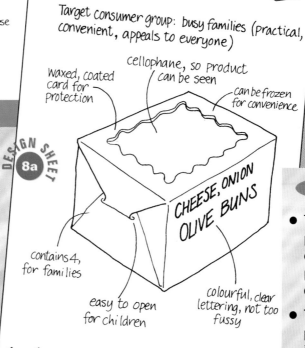

Target consumer group: busy families (practical, convenient, appeals to everyone)

Waxed, coated card for protection

Cellophane, so product can be seen

can be frozen for convenience

CHEESE, ONION OLIVE BUNS

contains 4, for families

easy to open for children

colourful, clear lettering, not too fussy

DESIGN SHEET 8a

Remember

- The success of a new product depends a lot on the way it is presented to consumers.

- The image of a new product must match its target group.

Starting Point

Over £100 million a year is spent on frozen vegetarian products. More and more people are becoming vegetarian. Food manufacturers want to meet this consumer demand.

Can you design and make a new frozen vegetarian product?

Food technologists have developed a variety of new vegetable products. These include sausages, burgers, savoury meals and quick snacks. What do vegetarians think of them? How successful are they?

Top Chef is a food manufacturing company. It produces frozen ready meals for schools in a local area. It wants a new meal to add to their schools' lunchtime range. This must be a new vegetarian product. It must appeal to teenagers.

TOP CHEF

MENU OF THE DAY

- Lasagne
- Chicken Curry
- Cottage Pie

Delivering frozen ready meals

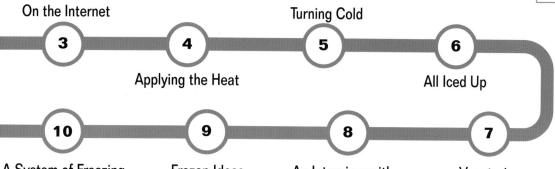

On the Internet
3

4
Applying the Heat

Turning Cold
5

6
All Iced Up

10
A System of Freezing

9
Frozen Ideas

8
An Interview with...
Tivall

7
Vegetarian
Consumers

The focus

In this unit you will focus on preservation. You will discover what makes food decay and how to preserve different foods. There are many methods of preservation. You will need to know about freezing.

Reheating foods will be important when designing your new product. Another area of focus will be vegetarian consumers.

The challenge

During this challenge it is important for you to test your ideas carefully. You must find out what teenagers think about your product. Your ideas must develop to match the needs of your target group.

You will also plan a production system. This must show how your product can be made safely and hygienically.

The end product

As always, the consumer has the final say. If your new meal is not popular with vegetarian teenagers it will not sell. At least you should not have a problem getting hold of your target group when it comes to testing! Hopefully your new meal will appeal to meat-eaters and staff who use the canteen too.

Why Does Food Go Off?

If food stayed fresh forever we would not have to worry about food poisoning! However, there are many ways to help food stay fresh for longer. What makes food 'go off' in the first place?

Time to go

Given enough time, all food will go off eventually. That is, it becomes unfit or unpleasant to eat. An apple that has started to brown may not be harmful yet may not taste very nice.

Food can go off in many ways. Meat will smell unpleasant. Bread will grow a green/blue mould. The lid of a yoghurt pot will bulge as gas is produced inside.

Natural causes

When food items such as fruit and vegetables go off this is known as **decay**.

The process of decay is a natural one. It begins as soon as food is picked or harvested. If fruit or vegetables are cut or peeled the air reacts with the flesh. The process of decay is then speeded up. For example, bananas turn brown if peeled and left. Enzymes inside the food make this happen more quickly. **Enzymes** are natural chemicals so they are not harmful.

Yeasts, bacteria and moulds

Food can be made unsafe to eat by micro-organisms. These are very small, living organisms. Some types of micro-organism are helpful and used in food production. Others are responsible for unwanted effects in food. For example, if present in large numbers, some bacteria can cause illness.

Micro-organisms are found everywhere – in the air, soil and water; on animals, humans and equipment.

Aspergillus fungus is common on decaying vegetables

Yeasts

Yeasts are the cause of that bulging yoghurt pot lid. They break down (or ferment) sugars to produce carbon dioxide gas and an alcohol called ethanol.

Fruits, jams and fruit yoghurts can be fermented by yeasts, making them unfit to eat.

Yeasts do not need oxygen but they do need warmth, moisture and food (sugar). They also have a useful role in food production. They help to make bread, alcoholic drinks and savoury spreads (such as Marmite and yeast extract).

Bacteria

One million bacteria can fit onto one pinhead! Some bacteria can be very harmful to humans.

Given the right conditions (moisture, warmth, food, oxygen) bacteria can multiply extremely quickly. Each bacterium cell divides into two in just a few minutes. Bacteria can multiply in certain foods and cause food poisoning. These bacteria include:

▷ *Salmonella* (found in poultry, eggs, raw meat)
▷ *Listeria monocytogenes* (found in soft cheeses, patés, pre-packed salads)
▷ *Escherichia coli – E. coli* (found in raw meat).

Food poisoning can be prevented by following hygiene rules and by preparing, cooking and storing food correctly (see Unit 5).

Moulds

Moulds are micro-organisms that can sometimes be seen. They are **fungi**, which need moisture, food and warmth to grow. However, food in the fridge can still develop a mould – it just takes longer. Some moulds produce poisonous substances so they should not be eaten. Other moulds are useful and safe. They help in the production of cheese. Danish Blue, Roquefort and Camembert are examples of mould-ripened cheese.

● *On task*

1. As a class or in groups, make your own yoghurt. Follow your teacher's instructions. Record what you did on design sheet **1a**.

2. Investigate how micro-organisms can be useful in food production. Work with a partner and choose a product made with the help of yeasts, moulds or bacteria (e.g. bread, beer, wine, yeast extract, cheese, yoghurt). Find out how the micro-organism helps production of that product in industry. Make notes on design sheet **1b**.

Remember

- Enzymes speed up the natural process of decay.

- Micro-organisms are very small organisms.

- Yeasts, bacteria and moulds can cause food to become unfit to eat.

On your design sheets

- Record the production of your home-made yoghurt. **1a**

- Make notes to show how micro-organisms are used in industrial food production. **1b**

Why do some shop-bought foods keep longer than some home-made foods? There are many methods of preserving food to make it stay fresh for longer. How do they compare?

E200 – Sorbic acid
(soft drinks, fruit yoghurts)

E213 – Calcium benzoate
(salad cream)

E283 – Potassium propionate
(pre-packed bread)

Preservation

There are various ways of making food last longer. These are known as methods of **preservation**. Here are some examples:

Preservation by making food hot

Bottling

UHT

Pasteurisation

Sterilisation

Canning

Preservation by making food cold

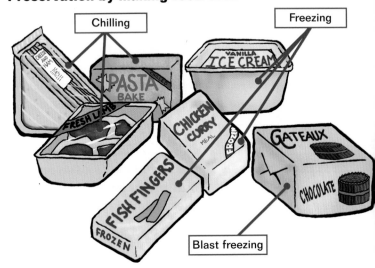

Chilling

Freezing

Blast freezing

Preservation by using chemicals

Vinegar

Sugar

Additives

Salt

Smoking

Preservation by other means

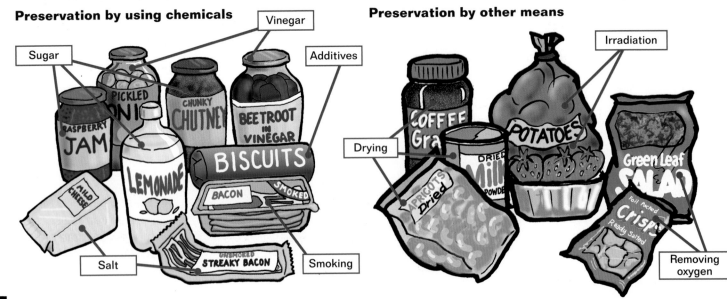

Irradiation

Drying

Removing oxygen

How long do they keep?

The methods of preservation shown on the previous page provide foods with different shelf-lives.

For example, fresh meat can be chilled giving it a shelf-life of a few days. Or it can be frozen so it can be kept for months.

Not all methods of preservation are suitable for all foods. However, some foods can be preserved in many ways.

E numbers

Many foods, including biscuits, have **preservatives** added to them during manufacture. This means they stay in good condition for longer than they would normally. They have a longer shelf-life. Preservatives are listed in the ingredients, often as **E numbers**.

● On task 1

Traditionally, fruit and vegetables in season were preserved so they could be eaten out of season. For example, peas grow in the UK during summer; that is their season. Lemons can be preserved by making them into a lemonade drink.
Make some lemonade using this recipe.

Home-made Lemonade

Ingredients
2 lemons
15 ml (1 tablespoon) citric acid
300 g (10½ oz) sugar
400 ml (14 fl oz) boiling water

Method
1. Wash the lemons. Finely grate the peel and squeeze the juice.
2. Place the lemon rind, juice and citric acid in a heat-proof bowl.
3. Add sugar and pour over the boiling water; stir until dissolved.
4. Pour into a sterilised bottle. Cool. Put in the fridge.

The lemonade can be diluted with still or sparkling water.

● On task 2

1. Choose five methods of preservation from page 76. Investigate foods preserved using those methods.

2. Find out the shelf-life of one food for each method. If possible, find out the price of each one.

3. Present your findings on your design sheet.

DESIGN SHEET 1

Methods of preservation

Method	Shelf-life	Cost	Comments
1 Drying eg. dried soup	1 year	4.9p	Useful to keep in the cupboard for emergencies; Very quick to prepare
2			
3			
4			
5			

On your design sheet

- Record your investigation into preserving lemons.
- Record your comparison of five methods of preservation.

Remember

- Preservation is a way of making foods last longer.
- There are many ways to preserve foods.

On the Internet

3

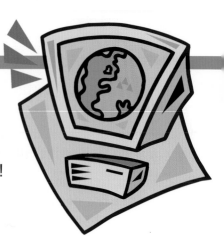

There is a whole world of information waiting for your investigation. Find out how you can extend your Food Technology projects by using the World Wide Web, without getting stuck in its sticky trap!

What is the Internet?

The Internet is a huge network of computers linked to each other. When using the Internet, a computer user is able to receive or pass on information.

What is the WWW?

The World Wide Web (WWW or Web for short) is really just a series of documents. They are all published on the Internet at **Web sites**.

There is an enormous range of topics available on the Web. More than one person or organisation may have information under the same topic heading.

Getting access

Many schools now have access to the Internet. This means when you have permission, you may use the Internet to investigate topics in Food Technology. Many food companies and supermarkets have Web sites, making it easy for consumers to find out more about them. They often provide information that would be useful for a Food Technology project.

Searching for an engine?

There are so many Web sites available on the Internet that it can take a long time to find the information you need.

To make hunting easier, a **search engine** can be used. You enter a keyword or words and the search engine scans the Internet for Web sites related to the keyword, then lists them for you.

However, if you typed in *food* you are likely to get a choice of over 600 Web sites! It would take a long time to look through all of these. So, you must try to be as precise as possible. For example, type in *food* and *coffee*.

www.icecreamusa.com

CLICK HERE FOR VIRTUAL DESSERT

● On task

As part of your investigation for this project, use the Internet to find out more about food preservation. Once you have connected to the Internet, choose the Web site you wish to use. Many supermarkets now have their own Web sites.

1. Use a supermarket Web site, for example:
www.sainsburys.co.uk

Find a recipe for a preserved food product such as lemon curd.

2. Write down on your design sheet the addresses of any useful Web sites that you visit. Make a note of the type of information they provide in case you need to use it later.

Ask your teacher if you want to save anything you found of particular interest.

Useful Web sites

http//www.icecreamusa.com
Here you can find out all about ice-cream on screen.

http://www.nutrition.org.uk
The British Nutrition Foundation provides up-to-date information about nutrition.

http://www.sainsburys.co.uk/
Sainsbury's provides access to over 800 recipes, nutrition, dietary and food safety information.

http://www.jakeh.demon.co.uk
This Web site allows you to investigate different types of packaging design.

http://www.veg.org/veg/Orgs/VegSocUK
The Vegetarian Society offers information and recipes for vegetarians.

www.sainsburys.co.uk

www.nutrition.org.uk

On your design sheet

● Keep a record of the Web sites you visit and what information you discover.

Remember

● The Internet is a very useful source of information.

● You need to check if what you find is accurate and reliable.

Applying the Heat

Food will often keep longer once it has been cooked. Applying heat to food is the basis for several methods of preservation.

Canning and bottling

Cans and jars of food are very convenient for consumers. They can last for years, and they contain all sorts of foods. These include puddings, milks, sauces, fruit, sausages and baby foods.

Sterilisation

Just as in canning and bottling, food is **sterilised** by heating it to high temperatures. Milk, for example, is heated to 105–110°C for 20–40 minutes. This heating changes the flavour of milk because the sugar is caramelised.

When food is canned or bottled it is sterilised by heat. This means all harmful micro-organisms and enzymes are killed by the high temperature.

Sterilisation can be done in two ways:

▷ the food is sterilised and then placed in a sterile container
▷ the food is placed in the container and then both are sterilised.

Cans and bottles are sealed, airtight containers that stop micro-organisms attacking the food. Once opened, the food is no longer sterile and must be treated as fresh.

Pasteurisation

Most people think of milk when **pasteurisation** is mentioned. This is because Louis Pasteur experimented with milk. He discovered that the souring of milk could be delayed if it was treated with heat. Pasteurisation destroys many harmful micro-organisms.

Today the process is used on other products such as sauces, cream, beer, wine and fruit juice.

IT can be used to help monitor and control the pasteurisation process

UHT

Ultra heat treatment is another method of preservation usually associated with milk. Today you can buy UHT fruit juice. If kept unopened, UHT foods can be stored for at least six months. This makes them very useful for consumers on holiday, catering or to have as a store cupboard standby.

UHT milk is heated to a very high temperature, 132.2°C, for one second. The flavour of the milk is not affected too much.

A milk pasteurisation machine

● **On task**

In this unit you are designing and making vegetarian meals that can be frozen. It is possible your designs may include ingredients that have been heat treated.

Begin designing ideas for your vegetarian product. You have still got more investigation to carry out, but the sooner you start thinking of ideas the better.

On your design sheet:
1. Sketch four or five ideas for a vegetarian school meal. You may need to visit your school canteen to help you. You could use a draw program.

2. Label each idea with its ingredients.

3. If any of the ingredients have been preserved explain the method used (e.g. baked beans by canning).

Design ideas for a vegetarian school meal

DESIGN SHEET 4

1. Bean Burger
bean burger
burger bun
tomato
lettuce

2. Vegetarian Pancake Roll
beansprouts
pancake
carrots
onion
broccoli

3. Cottage Quorn
mashed potato
peas
quorn
tomato
onion

4. Potato Hotdog
vegetarian sausage
jacket potato

On your design sheet

● Sketch four or five labelled designs.

● Indicate which ingredients are preserved and the method used.

Remember

● Canned and bottled food has been sterilised.

● Once opened, all preserved foods must be treated as fresh.

● Foods with a long shelf-life are useful for holidays, catering and storing.

Turning Cold

5

Many vegetarian food products can be found in supermarket freezer cabinets. Both chilling and freezing are useful methods of preservation. What is the difference between them?

A quick chill

Chilling is suitable for keeping foods at a low temperature, for example, sandwiches, salads, fresh meat or fish and ready meals. They are kept fresh for a short time, perhaps one day. By law these foods must be stored below 5°C.

Chill cabinets

Chill cabinets must be kept at the right temperature. They can be controlled by computers. Digital displays show the temperature and an alarm sounds if it rises. Sometimes staff have to check the thermometer on the outside of the cabinet.

Chilly food

Products known as **cook–chill** are cooked and very quickly chilled. They must reach a chilly 0–3°C in 90 minutes. The products have only a short shelf-life of up to five days. This includes the day of manufacture. These foods must be reheated by the consumer.

Inactive bacteria

Freezing preserves food in two ways. Firstly, the low temperature reduces the growth rate of micro-organisms. Secondly, the water in the food is turned into ice so it is not available to the micro-organisms.

A deep freeze

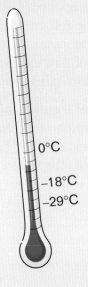

0°C

−18°C
−29°C

When food is frozen the temperature used is much lower than a chill cabinet. A freezer in a supermarket or factory must be between −18 and −29°C. The thermometer on the right shows these temperatures. Quick freezing means the food goes from 0 to −18°C in just 12 minutes.

Ice crystals

Food must be frozen quickly to be in good condition when it is defrosted. Ice crystals are formed inside the food when it is frozen. If the freezing process is fast, the crystals formed will be small. However, if the food is frozen slowly the ice has time to make large crystals. These may damage the cell walls of the food.

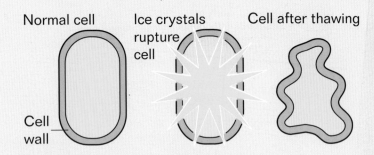

Normal cell   Ice crystals rupture cell   Cell after thawing

Cell wall

A blast freeze

Blast freezing is a very quick method of freezing food. It is particularly useful for fruit and vegetables. The food is placed in blast freezers and extremely cold air is blown directly onto it.

● On task

1. Choose one of your design ideas – one you think will work well as a frozen vegetarian product.

2. Plan how you will make your design idea. Write out the method, step-by-step. Present it as a flow chart on design sheet **5a**.

3. Make the product. Follow your flow chart carefully.

4. Finally, follow the Test Checklist on the right to see whether it can be frozen successfully.

TEST CHECKLIST

1. Take a small portion and place in a container suitable for freezing (e.g. Tupperware). Leave until completely cold.

2. Freeze your product sample, properly wrapped.

3. Evaluate the remainder of your product. Comment on its appearance, aroma, texture and taste. You will need to make detailed notes as you will be comparing this with the frozen sample.

4. Use the comparison table on design sheet **5b** to record the results of your evaluation.

5. During your next lesson, defrost and reheat your sample from the freezer. Make sure the food is piping hot all the way through.

6. Evaluate the results as before, then complete the table on design sheet **5b**.

DESIGN SHEET 5b

Product: Perfect Pizza

Quality	Non-frozen sample	Frozen, reheated sample
Appearance	deep base with colourful topping containing layers of tomato puree, fried onions, green pepper slices and chunks of cheese	
Aroma		
Texture		
Taste		
Other comments		

On your design sheets

● Present your chosen design idea. **5a**

● Produce a flow chart to show the production method. **5a**

● Present the results of your evaluation as a comparison table. **5b**

Remember

● Chilled products have a short shelf-life.

● Foods must be frozen quickly to prevent cell damage.

● Freezing stops micro-organisms growing until the food is defrosted.

All Iced Up

Freezing is a very convenient way to preserve food for a long time. All sorts of foods can be frozen. However, there are always exceptions...

Food for freezing

Many people today have a freezer at home. It can be filled with convenience foods such as ice cream or pizzas. It can also be used for storing left-over food. Some people make products and freeze them for later use. Home-grown fruit and vegetables can be preserved conveniently in the freezer.

Freezing does not change the appearance of food very much. It also has little effect on its **nutritional value.** In fact the nutritional value of many vegetables is as good, if not better than fresh. This is because they are frozen immediately they are harvested.

Some vegetables are blanched before freezing. Blanching involves plunging the prepared vegetables in boiling water for a short time. Then they are rapidly cooled in iced water. Blanching helps to stop enzymes speeding up the browning of the vegetables. This occurs naturally when they are cut. Look back at page 74 as a reminder of this.

Nothing lasts forever

Food can be stored successfully in a freezer. The storage life of a food will depend on how long it can be frozen and still be in perfect condition. Once this time has passed, chemical changes affect the flavour, quality and appearance of the food.

● On task

Carry out this investigation to find out which foods do not freeze well.

1. Choose six foods to investigate, or use those provided by your teacher. Ideas for foods include avocado pear, bananas, boiled potato, celery, cheese, cream, cucumber, egg (without shell), glacé icing, lettuce, mayonnaise, melon, radish, strawberries, tomatoes and yoghurt.

2. Prepare the foods for freezing (wash lettuce, peel banana, boil potatoes, etc.) You will only need small amounts.

3. Place foods in suitable containers, such as freezer bags. Label and date.

4. In one week's time, or when appropriate, remove and defrost the foods. Note their appearance, texture and taste (if possible).

5. Present your findings on design sheet **6a**. Use the information on the next page to explain your results.

6. How can you apply what you have discovered to the development of your design ideas? Do you now need to alter the ingredients to make them suitable for freezing? Record this information on design sheet **6b**.

Not for the freezer

Too much water

Foods that naturally contain high levels of water do not freeze well. They become mushy and discoloured when thawed. This is due to large ice crystals breaking up cell walls.

Separating

Dairy products can separate when they are frozen. This is due to their fat content. Full cream milk, for example, contains 3% fat. This floats to the top if left to stand. Fat is lighter than the liquid milk. When thawed, full cream milk will separate into fat and watery liquid.

Turning black

Some fruit and vegetables have a lot of enzyme activity which makes them discolour easily. Freezing does not prevent this and they often turn black, if untreated.

Cracking up

Foods with a shell, like eggs, will crack if frozen. As water becomes ice it expands. For example, when making ice cream at home you should allow space at the top of the container for the mixture to expand. If a whole egg is frozen on its own it will become gluey and sticky, but egg white and yolk can be frozen separately.

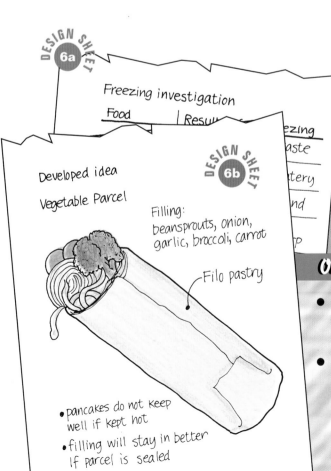

DESIGN SHEET 6a

Freezing investigation

Food | Resu...

DESIGN SHEET 6b

Developed idea

Vegetable Parcel

Filling: beansprouts, onion, garlic, broccoli, carrot

Filo pastry

- pancakes do not keep well if kept hot
- filling will stay in better if parcel is sealed

On your design sheets

- Present your results and write up the conclusions from your freezing experiment. **6a**

- Show how you are developing your design ideas further. Record your developments by describing, sketching and labelling your developed idea. **6b**

Remember

- Freezing does not affect the appearance and nutritional value of most foods.

- Freezing is a very convenient method of preserving many foods.

- Not all foods can be frozen successfully.

Vegetarian Consumers

7

More and more consumers are becoming vegetarian. What does it mean to be vegetarian? Is it a healthier way of life?

What is a vegetarian?

Being a **vegetarian** means different things to different people. The Vegetarian Society says a vegetarian is someone who eats no product that has resulted in the death of a living being, including fish.

Vegans

Vegans are vegetarians whose rules are more strict. They will not eat products even if the animal was not actually killed. For example, they will avoid dairy products (cheese, eggs and milk) and gelatine (made from animal bones). They will not wear leather clothes or shoes.

Demi-vegetarians

The amount of red meat being eaten today is generally declining. Some people have given up red meat altogether but are not true vegetarians because they include poultry and fish in their diet.

Why be a vegetarian?

People decide to lead a vegetarian lifestyle for many reasons. These include:

▷ concern for animals
▷ belief that a vegetarian diet is healthier
▷ fear from food scares
▷ concern for the environment
▷ religious or cultural beliefs
▷ they do not like meat.

Vegetarian benefits?

Some people believe that vegetarians are less likely to suffer heart disease, certain cancers, being extremely overweight (obesity) and kidney stones. However, anyone's diet can be low in fat and high in carbohydrates, vitamins and minerals if it is a balanced diet.

It must be remembered that meat is a good source of protein, iron and many B-vitamins. Vegetarians must make sure they replace meat with healthy alternatives. Nuts and cheese provide protein but they are high in fat.

What's on offer?

There are many products on sale that have been designed for vegetarians. There are many other products that carry the vegetarian symbol. For example, cheesecakes that are normally set with gelatine may be made with a vegetarian alternative instead (such as agar, made from seaweed).

The vegetarian symbol means they are suitable for vegetarians but they have not necessarily been approved by the Vegetarian Society.

Mix for
Hot Caramel Bananas
A sweet caramel and rum flavour sauce mix
with a hint of spice.

YOU WILL NEED
4 fresh ripe bananas   250ml (8½ floz) water   15g (½ oz) butter

DIRECTIONS   Serves 4
Blend the packet contents with the water in a microwaveable serving dish, add the butter.
Microwave on HIGH (750W) for 4 minutes, stirring well half-way through.
Cut the peeled bananas into 3 and arrange in the dish, turning to coat.
Microwave for a further 2-3 minutes, stirring gently half-way through.
Serve with ice cream or cream.

OVEN METHOD
Pre-heat the oven to 220°C, 425°F, Gas Mark 7. Blend the packet contents with 300ml (½ pint) water in a small saucepan, bring to the boil, stirring. Add the butter and stir until melted. Cut the peeled bananas into 3 and arrange in a lightly greased dish. Pour over the sauce and bake for 15-20 minutes, stirring half-way through.

NUTRITIONAL INFORMATION	Per 100g 1592kJ/376kcal	Per pack 42g 669kJ/158kcal
Energy	1.0g	0.4g
Protein	85.9g	36.1g
Carbohydrate	3.1g	1.3g
Fat		

CALCIUM
Calcium helps to make strong bones and teeth. It also helps blood to clot and keeps the nervous system healthy.

IRON
Iron is part of the haemoglobin in the blood that carries oxygen around the body.

VITAMIN B$_{12}$
This vitamin helps the body to use protein. It is involved with many reactions in the body, including the release of energy from food.

● On task

1. Carry out an investigation of your local shops and supermarket. Write your lists on design sheet **7a**.

   ▶ List the products that are made specifically for vegetarians.

   ▶ List the products that have a vegetarian symbol.

   Your investigation could be extended to health food shops. You may even find some products for vegans. Read the interview with Tivall on page 88 to help you.

2. Choose a vegetarian product that gives nutritional values on the label.

   Vegetarians should make sure they get enough calcium, iron and vitamin B$_{12}$ in their diet. Does the product you have chosen contain these nutrients? If so, how much?

3. Now evaluate your developed design idea by finding out how much calcium, iron or vitamin B$_{12}$ the ingredients provide. Use books or a software program. Write the amounts on design sheet **7b**.

   Do you need to alter any ingredients? Explain on your design sheet any changes you need to make.

After making my Vegetable Parcel, I worked out the nutritional value of one portion. To do this I used nutritional software. The results are shown on the next page.

I have decided that my Vegetable Parcel does not provide enough iron so now I need to add more green vegetables to the filling.

DESIGN SHEET **7b**

On your design sheets

- Present two lists of vegetarian products. **7a**

- Record the calcium, iron and vitamin B$_{12}$ content of one product. **7a**

- Evaluate your developed design idea according to its nutritional value. Explain if you need to change any ingredients. **7b**

Remember

- A vegetarian will not eat a product that has resulted in the death of an animal.

- Many food products can use a vegetarian alternative ingredient.

8

Tivall is a specialist food company that knows all about vegetarian frozen products. What can you learn from its experience?

Who are Tivall?

" We are an international manufacturer of meat-free products based in Israel. Tivall exports its range world-wide but its main market is Europe. The UK and Holland are the biggest consumers of its products.

The company was founded in 1986. It is dedicated to creating healthy meat-free products. Tivall is involved in developing the latest technical know-how and using modern production methods. "

What sort of products do you produce?

" Tivall's vegetarian products are made completely free from meat. No animal fats are used in their production. The products mimic the taste of real meat and are called **meat analogues**. They are made using a blend of wheat and soya or pea proteins. These form a **base** which can then have vitamins and minerals added to it.

Tivall has pioneered a unique process creating a new meat analogue called Fibrous Vegetable Protein (FVP) which simulates the actual appearance and 'bite' of meat muscle.

The products are flavoured with natural flavours and spices. The product range includes Sausages, Burgers, Schnitzels, Nuggets and Pieces. "

How do you find out what customers are looking for in a vegetarian product?

66 Tivall predicts what products will appeal to customers in a number of ways.

Firstly, market research is used to ask members of the public what they think about vegetarian foods. This research can help the company find out what consumers are really looking for.

Secondly, the Research and Development department produces a number of trial new products. These are shown to independent food research companies. Here the new products are tested by experts and by members of the public who take part in a taste panel. Many different factors are considered when testing a new product, such as:

▷ does the product look appealing?
▷ how does it taste?
▷ is there an unpleasant after-taste?
▷ what is the texture like?
▷ does it cook in the manufacturer's recommended time?

After all this, Tivall should have a great new product to launch onto the market. 99

What type of freezing process do you use?

66 Tivall uses individual quick freezing. Cold air (-40°C) is passed over the products until they reach a final temperature of -18°C. 99

What advice would you give someone designing and making a vegetarian meal that is to be frozen?

66 We would advise them to think about the following questions:

▷ Who are you designing the meal for? (For example, children, adults, the health-conscious?)
▷ What is your financial budget?
▷ How will the meal be cooked? (By oven, grilling, frying, microwave?)
▷ How will the meal be balanced and nutritious? (For example, not too much fat or salt, enough protein and carbohydrates?)
▷ Will the meal stand up to being frozen and reheated? (Will it not become soggy or too dry?) 99

On your design sheet

● Show how you have used Tivall's questions as a checklist as you develop your design idea.

Frozen Ideas

9

Design ideas have to be tested and developed to make sure they suit the task. They must also match up to the product specification.

Product specification

During the development of a new food product a **specification** is written. A specification contains information about the new product. For example, a product specification for a new vegetarian meal might include:

▷ ingredients, with quantities
▷ equipment needed
▷ cooking times and temperatures
▷ production flow chart
▷ freezing times and temperatures
▷ sensory qualities (moist, crunchy, spicy, golden brown, etc.)

● **On task 1**

Using your latest developed design idea, complete a product specification on design sheet **9a**.

SPECIFICATION CHECKLIST

☐ raw materials
☐ recipe (ingredients and quantities)
☐ methods
☐ production flow chart/system
☐ critical control points (see Unit 5)
☐ microbiological standards
☐ nutritional information
☐ packaging specification
☐ shelf-life
☐ finished product weight/volume
☐ sensory specification
☐ consumer instructions

PRODUCT SPECIFICATION

Product name:

Ingredients:

Equipment:

Cooking times:

Cooking temperatures:

Freezing temperatures:

Storage times:

Sensory qualities:

Testing teenagers

Remember, the task you have been given for this unit is to design a new vegetarian frozen product for Top Chef food manufacturers. They require a meal to add to their schools' lunchtime range. It must appeal to teenagers and be suitable for freezing.

You now need to find out what teenagers think of your new vegetarian meal.

● On task 2

1. Using the labelled sketch of your current idea and your product specification, ask some teenagers (preferably vegetarian) what they think of your design. Record their responses on design sheet **9c**. Ask about:

- ► the ingredients
- ► the appearance
- ► would they choose it from a lunchtime menu?
- ► any improvements they would like to see.

2. Make any further changes to your design, if necessary.

3. What do you already know about hygiene and safety rules that you should follow during the production of your product? Make notes on design sheet **9b**.

4. Make your developed product for the final time. If possible, test a small portion to see how well it freezes this time. (You could use an ice cube tray for this.)

5. Find out what teenagers think of your design now that it has been made. Ask them the same questions as before and record the results on design sheet **9c**.

DESIGN SHEET 9c

Questionnaire

Please have a good look at my labelled sketch of a Vegetable Parcel and answer the following questions:

- Do you like all the ingredients?

YES							
NO							

- Write the name of any ingredients you do **not** like: ......

- Do you think the product looks appetising?

YES							
NO							

On your design sheets

- Record your product specification. **9a**
- Record your hygiene and safety points. **9b**
- Present the information gathered from teenagers about your design idea and your developed product. **9c**

Remember

- A product specification contains information about a food product.

A System of Freezing

10

Systems are used a great deal in the food industry. They help to organise a process so it runs smoothly. A system can be planned for the production and freezing of your new vegetarian meal.

What is a system?

A **system** is a series of things which are connected together. In a computer system a number of units (keyboard, monitor, hard drive, CD-ROM, etc.) are connected to work together.

Systems can also be a sequence of events. A school timetable is a system. It connects together different groups of pupils and teachers in rooms at certain times through the day or week.

A recipe is a system, too. It shows how ingredients, tools, equipment and the cook or chef need to work together. Everything needs to be in the right place at the right time.

Flow charts

A **flow chart** is a way of drawing a simple system. It shows someone where to start, what to do next and so on. Production plans can take the form of a flow-chart. They show a sequence of events in making a food product.

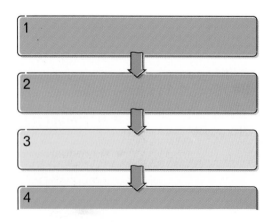

Symbols

A flow chart can be made even more useful by using symbols. These are the most commonly used symbols for flow charts:

Name	Symbol	What it shows
Terminator		Beginning or end of the system
Process		What needs to be done
Decision		A question is asked with a yes or no answer

On the right is a simple example of the symbols being used.

A system for filling a freezer

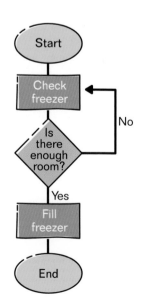

Closed-loop system

The name for a flow chart that uses questions is a **closed-loop** system. It is closed because you can only follow the system in a certain way and you know when you have come to the end.

Asking a question in the middle of a system involves making a decision. The answer to the question is called feedback. You will find out more about this on page 122.

● *On task*

1. On page 83 you produced a production flow chart for your new product. Now work out a closed-loop system for making and freezing your meal.

 An example is shown on the right. Draw your flow chart on design sheet **10**.

2. Now produce a closed-loop system for the defrosting and reheating of your new product. Try to include some timings.

3. Make your final design idea. While you are working note on your design sheet any important points about its production. This will help you suggest improvements for your final evaluation. You might feel you used the wrong tool. Or perhaps you could have done things in a different order.

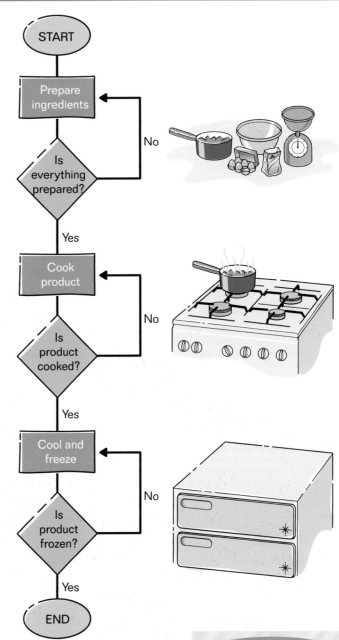

DESIGN SHEET 10

Notes
• cut out filo pastry more accurately — the parcels are going to end up different sizes
• chop beansprouts to make it easier to fill the parcels
• remember to preheat oven next time

On your design sheet

● Produce a closed-loop system for making and freezing your product.

● Produce a closed-loop system for defrosting and reheating your product.

● Note important points about its production.

Remember

● A system is a series of things which are connected together.

● A flow chart can show a system.

● Feedback is the response to a question asked within the system.

Ask the Consumer

11

Finally in this unit you will learn that a product can only be successful if it is liked by the consumer. Not only that but the consumer must buy it too! Will teenage vegetarians want to buy your new meal from the school canteen?

Testing times

Once a new product has been developed and tested it is time to ask the consumers what they think. Food companies will not spend large sums of money launching a new product unless they are convinced consumers will like it and buy it. A delicious new vegetarian meal is no good to teenagers if they can't afford to buy it.

Testing the senses

A product specification often contains a list of **sensory qualities**. This means the words chosen to describe the product's appearance, aroma, taste and texture.

RATING OF SENSORY QUALITIES: 1= low 5= high		
Product name:	Creamed curry vegetables	
Quality	Description of desired quality	Taster 1
Appearance	golden brown	3
Aroma	spicy	2
Texture	creamy	2
Taste	curry	1
How would you rate the whole product?	1 - 5	2

Comparing ideas

Another useful way to evaluate a final product is to compare it with others. There may be someone who has designed something similar. Or there may be something similar already on sale. How do they compare?

● On task 1

Ask a range of teenagers to taste your final product. Ideally they should be vegetarian. Then ask them to consider the sensory qualities from your product specification (see page 90). Complete the rating table on design sheet **11a**.

● On task 2

Compare your final design idea with a similar product. Decide exactly what you are going to compare. For example, you could compare the energy value, appearance or portion size.

Record the results on design sheet **11b** as part of your final evaluation.

● On task 3

1. Look back at the notes you made on design sheet **10** when making your final product. Consider all the information gathered during the production: timings, sensory qualities, other people's comments, etc.

2. On design sheet **11b**, explain how you would improve your product if you were to make it again. Use diagrams to help show the changes.

Final report

At the end of the final testing a product report must be completed. This involves looking back at the entire project and evaluating its success. It may be a written report or a form which has to be filled in.

● On task 4

Prepare a final report for your teenage vegetarian meal on design sheet **11c**. You will need to be very honest about the results. Suggest any improvements that need to be made. Use the report form provided (see right), or prepare a written report with headings such as:

▶ Outline of product idea

▶ Reasons for it being a good idea

▶ Problems and changes needed in the production

▶ Description of finished product: appearance, aroma, texture, flavour

▶ Matching of idea with sensory qualities

▶ Comparing final idea

▶ Conclusions and ideas for the future

```
            FINAL REPORT

Product name:
_____
Product description or sketch:



_____
Comments about ingredients used:


_____
Comments about equipment used:


_____
Changes to be made to the production:


_____
Description of final product
(appearance, aroma, texture, taste):



_____
Conclusions and comments:
```

On your design sheets

● Present the results of your sensory evaluation. **11a**

● Present the results of your product comparison. **11b**

● Explain any changes needed. **11b**

● Produce a final report or table for your product. **11c**

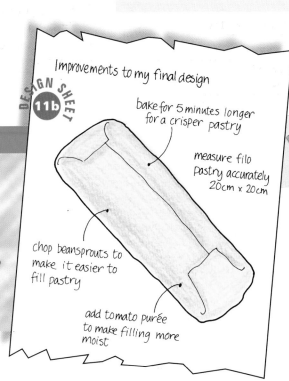

DESIGN SHEET 11b

Improvements to my final design

bake for 5 minutes longer for a crisper pastry

measure filo pastry accurately 20cm x 20cm

chop beansprouts to make it easier to fill pastry

add tomato purée to make filling more moist

Remember

● A new food product must be acceptable to consumers before it is launched onto the market.

Starting Point

Food can be tasty, exciting and fun – but is it always safe to eat? Usually you cannot tell just by looking at it. So, what should we be doing to make sure food is really safe?

Imagine you are the food technologist for a new sandwich bar called 'Anything But The Sandwich'. You need to come up with ideas for a new alternative to the traditional sandwich. It is to be produced, packaged and transported to the sandwich bar for sale.

The new staff at 'Anything But The Sandwich' need to know how to prepare food safely. They must learn how to identify and avoid possible hazards. Can you help them with this?

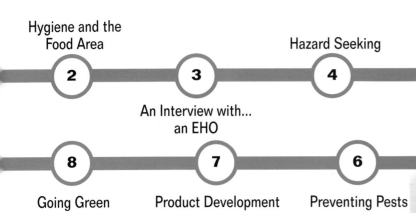

Hygiene and the
Food Area

2

3

An Interview with...
an EHO

Hazard Seeking

4

5

Safe Systems

8

7

6

Going Green

Product Development

Preventing Pests

The focus

In this unit you will focus on food safety and product development. You will learn why food safety is such an important topic. It relates to the food area, food handler and food products.

You will also discover how new food products are developed in industry. This will include finding out about today's **green issues**.

The challenge

During this challenge you will gain experience in designing new food products. Your designs must take account of all you learn about food safety.

This may involve changing your design to ensure hygiene standards are met.

You will also have the opportunity to test and evaluate your design ideas. This will involve careful planning of the production using a system of identifying hazards.

The end product

Your new product must be anything but a traditional sandwich! Having planned its production very carefully you should produce a quality product. Remember, you have a responsibility to others to ensure your end product is safe to prepare and eat.

Working Safely

1

EATING SAFELY

Food poisoning strikes thousands of people every year. In extreme cases it can be fatal. Anyone who prepares food, at home or at work, must know about food safety.

Food poisoning

Food poisoning can happen when contaminated food or drink is consumed. It can cause vomiting, diarrhoea, stomach pains and weakness.

Food poisoning in the UK is on the increase. The chart below shows the rise in cases between 1982 and 1996. However, not everybody goes to the doctor with food poisoning symptoms. This makes it difficult to get exact figures.

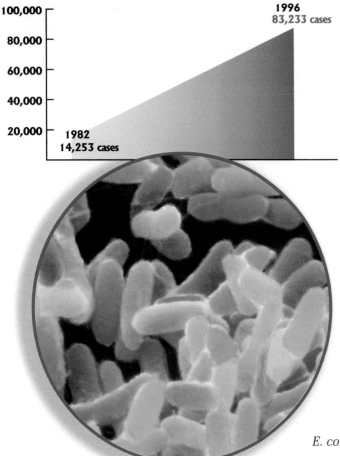

E. coli bacteria

Contamination

Food or drink can be contaminated by bacteria, moulds and yeasts. You learnt about these in the last unit. **Contaminated** means the food has become infected and may cause harm to the person who eats it. Food can become contaminated through:

▷ the food handler
▷ contact with other foods
▷ contact with work-surfaces and equipment
▷ pests and waste material.

The food handler

Bacteria live in and on your body. Your hands can easily pass bacteria on to food. Standards of personal hygiene must be very high. It is essential that all people who handle food wash their hands thoroughly using hot water and soap. Liquid soap is more hygienic in food areas than bars of soap. Anti-bacterial liquid soap is useful too.

Remember, hands must be washed:

▷ before entering the food area and before touching any food
▷ after handling raw meat, poultry, shellfish, eggs or vegetables
▷ after using the toilet
▷ after coughing, even if a handkerchief is used
▷ after touching hair or face
▷ after handling rubbish.

● *On task*

Prepare the test recipe for a new-look sandwich shown below, or use one provided by your teacher. Follow the points of hygiene outlined on the left. Watch others as they work. Have they remembered all the rules? Record your observations on your design sheet.

Points of hygiene

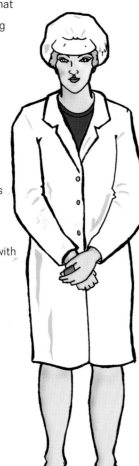

- Keep hair covered with a net or hat
- Avoid touching your face and head
- Wear clean, protective clothing
- Cover wounds with a blue, waterproof dressing
- Do not work with food if feeling unwell

- Never comb your hair in a food area
- Avoid coughing or sneezing in a food area – bacteria live in your nose, throat, mouth, ears, hair
- Avoid jewellery and nail varnish
- Wash hands whenever necessary
- Smoking is against the law in a food area

TEST RECIPE

Tuna Pockets

Ingredients

4 pitta bread
200g (7oz) tuna, drained
60ml (4 tablespoons) mayonnaise

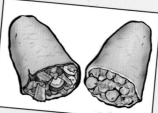

Filling ideas – choose 2 or 3:
2 spring onions
½ red pepper
1 green apple
1 stick celery
2 x 15ml (2 tablespoons) fresh coriander
small piece (14oz) of cucumber
½ 400g (14oz) can chick peas, drained

Method

1. Place tuna in a bowl with mayonnaise and mash.
2. Prepare chosen filling ingredients as appropriate.
3. Mix the filling ingredients with the tuna.
4. Grill pitta for 2 minutes on each side.
5. Cut in half then prise open a 'pocket'. Fill each pocket.
6. Eat straight away, or cool, wrap (when cold) and chill.

On your design sheet

- Explain the hygiene rules you and others followed when preparing the test recipe.

Remember

- Food poisoning occurs when contaminated food or drink is consumed.
- Contamination can be through people, pests, other foods, equipment.
- Personal hygiene is very important for the food handler.

Hygiene and the Food Area

2

EATING SAFELY

There's more to hygiene than just washing your hands! The layout of the food area can affect hygiene standards too.

A hygienic kitchen has:

- good lighting so food handlers can work hygienically and safely
- good ventilation to remove smells, steam and heat
- stainless steel work surfaces that are strong, durable and easy to clean
- stainless steel sinks; one for washing food, one for washing dishes and one for washing hands
- waste disposal so waste food can be removed quickly and efficiently
- non-slip floors that are durable and easy to clean
- no cracks for food and dirt to hide.

The ideal space

An ideal food area will have lots of space for preparing food. There will be plenty of storage room and separate areas for different types of ingredients – raw meats, cooked meats, etc.

A food business must be registered with the Local Authority. It will also be inspected by an Environmental Health Officer. You will learn more about the work of an Environmental Health Officer on pages 102–3.

Kitchen design

A hygienic kitchen will be a well organised one. Different areas will be allocated for different jobs. 'Anything But The Sandwich' could be divided into several main areas.

Delivery
↓
Storage
↓
Preparation
↓
Service

The delivery area will need to be close to the storage rooms so food can be put away quickly. Vegetables and fruit may carry dirt so must be washed and prepared in a separate area. Raw meat is always prepared away from cooked meat. This is to avoid **cross-contamination**.

Once preparation has been completed, the food can go to the service area. Here the various items are assembled for consumers.

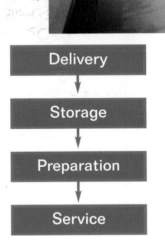

Clean equipment

Just like work surfaces, equipment must be thoroughly cleaned after use. Liquidisers, food processors, graters, knives – anything that has been in contact with food will attract bacteria. They should be stored in cupboards or protected from dust, dirt and insects.

Colour codes

Food premises now use a system of colour coding in their preparation areas. For example, separate chopping boards, knives and cloths should be used with different foods. Here are the colour codes:

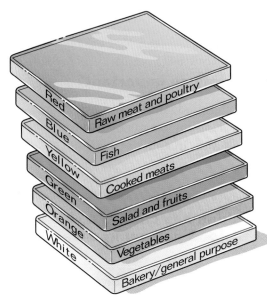

Red — Raw meat and poultry
Blue — Fish
Yellow — Cooked meats
Green — Salad and fruits
Orange — Vegetables
White — Bakery/general purpose

● On task

1. Working in pairs, choose suitable ingredients for a 'double-decker'. Use the ideas below to help you. Record your ideas on design sheet **2a**.

2. Plan how to prepare your double-decker hygienically and safely. One person (1) should be responsible for the salad ingredients and bread. The other person (2) should be responsible for the raw ingredients. Use the table below to help you record your plan on design sheet **2b**.

Double-decker

Ingredients ideas

Bread	Salad	Raw
3 slices each of thick white or wholemeal or granary	lettuce, cucumber, tomato, radish, onions, watercress, avocado, mushroom	chicken. bacon, eggs, sausages (meat or vegetarian)

Method

1. Wash and chop or slice the salad ingredients.
2. Cook raw ingredients as appropriate.
3. Toast the bread lightly on both sides.
4. Fill and layer as a double-decker.

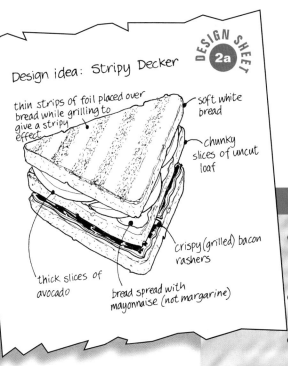

Design idea: Stripy Decker

DESIGN SHEET 2a

thin strips of foil placed over bread while grilling to give a stripy effect

soft white bread

chunky slices of uncut loaf

crispy (grilled) bacon rashers

thick slices of avocado

bread spread with mayonnaise (not margarine)

Production steps (1)	Hygiene check
1. Wash lettuce and tomato	To remove dirt
2. Pat lettuce dry	Using paper or drier, not tea towel

On your design sheets

- Record your idea for a double-decker. Use labelled sketches if you wish. **2a**
- Record the preparation instructions for you and your partner. **2b**
- Include hygiene checks on your preparation record. **2b**

Remember

- The design of a food area can affect hygiene standards.
- A food business must be registered with the Local Authority.

An Interview with... an EHO

EATING SAFELY

3

Linda Roberts works as an **Environmental Health Officer** for Sheffield City Council. You can learn a lot about food safety by reading about her job.

What is involved in a job like yours?

❝ I inspect food premises like cafés, restaurants, canteens, pubs and sandwich shops. I have to make sure the business owners, managers and employees are aware of the legal requirements and that they follow them. The legal requirements include:

▷ Food Safety Act 1990

▷ Food Safety (General Food Hygiene) Regulations 1995

▷ Food Safety (Temperature Control) Regulations 1995

▷ Health and Safety at Work Act 1974.

I investigate food complaints and cases of food poisoning. I also offer advice and guidance to food businesses on matters of food safety. I also teach basic food hygiene for the basic food hygiene certificate. ❞

Why is food safety so important?

❝ If food is not handled, stored and prepared safely, food poisoning can occur making people very ill and, in some cases, even cause death. ❞

What do you think has caused a rise in the number of food poisoning cases in recent years?

❝ There are many factors. They include:

▷ poor food hygiene practice (at home and in business)

▷ poor food hygiene awareness

▷ intensive animal rearing resulting in contaminated raw meat and poultry

▷ greater use of convenience foods

▷ greater use of microwaves

▷ more people eating out

▷ changing lifestyles (people now eat more poultry/white meat)

▷ changes in meal patterns (family members eat at different times so food is reheated)

▷ consumers do not want to see preservatives in their food

▷ poor food storage.

This list does not include every reason! ❞

What would you be looking for if you were to visit a sandwich bar?

" I would be looking for good standards of hygiene and cleanliness, an awareness of good food hygiene practice and employees, supervisors and managers who have the basic food hygiene certificate.

I would also want to see that an analysis of food hazards had been carried out and measures were in place to control those hazards, such as temperature control. "

What advice would you give someone designing and making a new-look product for sale in a sandwich bar?

" I would advise that the designer or producer carries out a **hazard analysis** for the new product. This would identify any food safety hazards regarding the product's production.

This would involve looking at all the steps in the food's production, from buying in the ingredients to offering the product for sale. At each step you would need to consider what might go wrong, then put in a control measure. This reduces the risk of causing food poisoning. This can be seen in the poster shown here: "

On your design sheet

- Linda Roberts has suggested some factors that may have caused an increase in food poisoning.

  Explain which ones you will need to consider when designing your product.

H16/012 712 2P 120k Aug 96 (04)

DEPARTMENT OF HEALTH

ASSURED SAFE CATERING • CRITICAL CONTROL POINTS

Step	Hazard	Action
1 Purchase	High-risk* (ready-to-eat) foods contaminated with food-poisoning bacteria or toxins (Poisons produced by bacteria).	Buy from reputable supplier only. Specify maximum temperature at delivery.
2 Receipt of food	High-risk* (ready-to-eat) foods contaminated with food-poisoning bacteria or toxins.	Check it looks, smells and feels right. Check the temperature is right.
3 Storage	Growth of food poisoning bacteria, toxins on high-risk* (ready-to-eat) foods. Further contamination.	High-risk* foods stored at safe temperatures. Store them wrapped. Label high-risk foods with the correct 'sell by' date. Rotate stock and use by recommended date.
4 Preparation	Contamination of High-risk* (ready-to-eat) foods. Growth of food-poisoning bacteria.	Wash your hands before handling food. Limit any exposure to room temperatures during preparation. Prepare with clean equipment, and use this for high-risk* (ready-to-eat) food only. Separate cooked foods from raw foods.
5 Cooking	Survival of food-poisoning bacteria.	Cook rolled joints, chicken, and re-formed meats eg. burgers,so that the thickest part reaches at least 75°C. Sear the outside of other, solid meat cuts (eg. joints of beef, steaks) before cooking.
6 Cooling	Growth of any surviving spores or food poisoning bacteria. Production of poisons by bacteria. Contamination with food-poisoning bacteria.	Cool foods as quickly as possible. Don't leave out at room temperatures to cool, unless the cooling period is short, eg place any stews or rice, etc, in shallow trays and cool to chill temperatures quickly.
7 Hot-holding	Growth of food-poisoning bacteria. Production of poisons by bacteria.	Keep food hot, at or above 63°C.
8 Reheating	Survival of food-poisoning bacteria.	Reheat to above 75°C.
9 Chilled storage	Growth of food-poisoning bacteria.	Keep temperature at right level. Label high-risk ready-to-eat foods with correct date code.
10 Serving	Growth of disease-causing bacteria. Production of poisons by bacteria.	COLD SERVICE FOODS - serve high-risk foods as soon as possible after removing from refrigerated storage to avoid them getting warm. HOT FOODS - serve high-risk foods quickly to avoid them cooling

Hazard Seeking

4

EATING SAFELY

'Anything But The Sandwich' won't last long if its customers develop food poisoning! The law says food businesses must follow a system which will ensure good food hygiene standards.

What is a hazard?

A system that demonstrates good food hygiene is one which can identify hazards. A hazard is anything that can cause harm to the consumer. Hazards can be:

▷ biological, e.g. micro-organisms such as bacteria and moulds

▷ chemical, e.g. pesticides, insecticides, cleaning agents

▷ physical, e.g. 'foreign bodies' such as pieces of glass or an insect.

A hazard can occur at any stage of food preparation. A bag of flour may accidentally contain a piece of metal when it is delivered. A hazard could occur when ingredients are delivered, prepared, cooked, processed, stored or served.

Not enough time allowed for thawing
(frozen food must be thawed before cooking – especially poultry)

Prepared food left hanging around
(food should not be prepared until it is needed)

Rubbish and food scraps lying around
(waste foods must be disposed of immediately)

Hot food left in a warm area
(unless serving food straight away, it must be cooled quickly then stored)

Foods incorrectly stored
(hot food must be kept hot and cold food kept cold)

Undercooked meat
(meat must be thoroughly cooked and reach 70°C in the centre)

Uncovered foods
(cooked food should be covered or stored correctly)

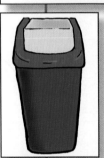

● On task

'Anything But The Sandwich' needs help identifying possible hazards. It has completed one hazard analysis, shown on the right.

On your design sheet:

1. Choose one of the recipes that you have already tested.

2. List the steps in making that product

3. For each step, suggest a possible hazard.

HAZARD ANALYSIS

Steps in producing an egg and cress croissant	Possible hazards
· collect eggs from storage	· might not be fresh
· hard-boil eggs	· could be undercooked
· prepare cress	· may contain dirt
· cool eggs	· bacteria like the warmth
· collect mayonnaise from storage	· may have passed best-before date
· mash eggs with mayonnaise	· cross-contamination with equipment or food
· cut croissant	· contamination from equipment
· fill with egg and cress	· contamination from equipment or hands

The Food Safety (General Food Hygiene) Regulations, 1995 say that food producers must ensure that food is handled hygienically.

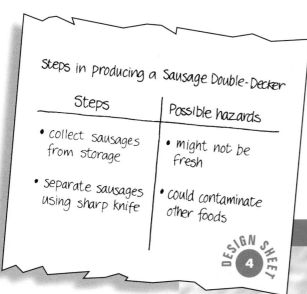

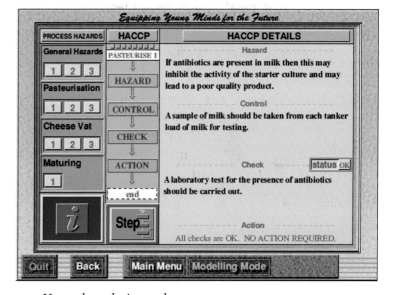

Hazard analysis can be explored using published software

On your design sheet

● Record a hazard analysis for your product.

Remember

● A hazard is anything that can cause harm to the consumer.

● Possible hazards have to be identified so they can be avoided.

Safe Systems

Identifying hazards and saying how to avoid them is a system of food safety. These systems are used in the food industry and in food businesses. How do they work?

HACCP

HACCP is a food safety system. It stands for **Hazard Analysis Critical Control Point**. The original system was developed from ideas used in the engineering industry. It was developed in America to ensure safe food was provided for astronauts! You will find out more about **HACCP** on pages 126–7. **Systems** are discussed on pages 122–3.

Assured Safe Catering

'Anything But The Sandwich' is going to use the **Assured Safe Catering** system.

This system looks at the catering procedure step-by-step – from selecting the ingredients to serving the customer.

Anything which might affect the safety of the food is identified and can be avoided.

Assured Safe Catering helps prevent safety problems by careful planning in easy steps.

An example of the Assured Safe Catering system for a small business which serves only cold food

Stage	Possible Hazard	Action needed
Food is purchased	High risk foods which are to be eaten without further cooking are bought. Possible contamination with bacteria and/or toxins	Buy only high quality ingredients from reputable suppliers. Specify maximum temperature for transit and delivery
Food is received on premises	High risk food may already be contaminated	Check temperatures Check quality Check date-mark
Storage of food	Growth of food poisoning organisms and/or possible further contamination	Wrap, label, and store high risk food at correct temperature. Rotate stock and use by recommended date
Preparation of food	Contamination of high risk food by incorrect and extensive handling. Growth of bacteria	Wash hands before handling food. Use clean equipment. Limit time food is within the temperature danger zone. Separate from any raw food
Cold holding of food	Growth of bacteria. Possible contamination	Ensure correct temperature. Limit time
Serving of prepared food	Growth of bacteria. Possible contamination	Serve directly from cold storage (refrigerator) or from cold holding (cold counter or display unit)

HAZARD ANALYSIS

Steps in producing an egg and cress croissant	Possible hazards	Action needed
· collect eggs from storage	· might not be fresh	· check best-before date
· hard-boil eggs	· could be undercooked	· time carefully
· prepare cress	· may contain dirt	· wash to remove dirt
· cool eggs	· bacteria like the warmth	· cool eggs quickly using cold water
· collect mayonnaise from storage	· may have passed best-before date	· rotate stock/check dates regularly
· mash eggs with mayonnaise	· cross-contamination with equipment or food	· use clean equipment
· cut croissant	· contamination from equipment	· use white chopping board and clean knife
· fill with egg and cress	· contamination from equipment or hands	· use spoon and wear plastic gloves

'Anything But The Sandwich' identified possible hazards in making an egg and cress croissant. Now it must state the action needed to stop the hazard occurring. Its hazard analysis is shown on the left.

Software is available to help you understand the HACCP system.

● **On task**

1. Design three new recipe ideas for 'Anything But The Sandwich' (e.g. filled jacket potato, filled bagel, open sandwich). Record your designs as annotated sketches on design sheet **5a**.

2. Choose one of your design ideas to test and evaluate. State why it is suitable for sale at 'Anything But The Sandwich'. List the ingredients needed, with quantities, on design sheet **5b**.

4. Produce a hazard analysis for your idea on design sheet **5c**. You need to:

   ▶ plan the steps involved in making your design

   ▶ suggest a possible hazard for each step

   ▶ state the action needed to avoid the hazard.

Steps in producing a Sausage Double-Decker

Steps	Possible hazards	Action needed
· collect sausages from storage	· might not be fresh	· check use-by date
· separate sausages using sharp knife	· could contaminate other foods	· use red chopping board and red handled knife

DESIGN SHEET **5c**

On your design sheets

● Produce three design ideas using labelled sketches. **5a**

● State which idea you will test. Give reasons. **5b**

● List the ingredients with quantities. **5b**

● Produce a hazard analysis showing production steps, possible hazards and action needed. **5c**

Remember

● HACCP and Assured Safe Catering are food safety systems.

Preventing Pests

6

EATING SAFELY

Food safety is not just about food poisoning. How do we know what happens to our food before we buy it? Is anybody checking to see if it is safe to eat?

Chemicals

In the past, if crops like potatoes were destroyed by insects or disease there would be no more potatoes that year. Today we can control disease and pests, so food is always available. Crops can be sprayed with pesticides. These are chemicals which include:

▷ insecticides (to kill insects)
▷ rodenticides (to kill pests like rats and mice)
▷ herbicides (to kill weeds)
▷ fungicides (to prevent the growth of fungus or mould).

The chemicals used must be tested and controlled carefully. The amount a farmer can use on a particular crop is restricted. There are also legal limits which state how much pesticide can be left in the crops.

How green is your strawberry?

Some people are very concerned about chemicals on plants. At one time, strawberries would only appear in the shops during the summer. That is their season for growing in this country. Today, strawberries are imported so we can buy them all year round.

Of course, supermarkets want to sell strawberries that are plump and red. They also want them to have a long shelf-life. This means they have to be sprayed with pesticides which may damage our environment as well as our health.

In 1997, Government tests discovered pesticide residues left in 88% of strawberries. The residues included a fungicide called lindane which has been linked to cancer.

United Kingdom approved organic certification bodies (as at 1st January 1995)	
Biodynamic Agricultural Association	
Irish Organic Farmers and Growers Association	
Organic Farmers and Growers	
Organic Food Federation	
Scottish Organic Producers Association	
Soil Association Organic Marketing Company	

Organic answers

Today, more and more organic foods are available in our supermarkets. Organic varieties include fruit, vegetables, tea, ice cream, chocolate, meat, even beer!

Organic crops are grown without using:

▷ pesticides, fungicides or herbicides
▷ synthetic fertilisers
▷ growth regulators or stimulants (making crops grow faster).

Organic meat and poultry are reared without using antibiotics or intensive farming methods.

An organic farm will use traditional methods such as:

▷ crop rotation (to help keep soil pest-free)
▷ natural pest control (ladybirds eat greenfly to control their numbers)
▷ natural composts and manure (to fertilise the soil).

Organic foods cost more because the farming methods need more time and labour. However, as more people buy them, so prices will fall. Many people believe organic food tastes better and is safer and more natural to eat.

● On task

1. Look at the fruit and vegetables provided by your teacher. Carry out a taste-test to see if you can detect which are organically grown and which are not. Complete the table on design sheet **6a**.

2. Test your last design for 'Anything But The Sandwich'. Follow your hazard analysis (design sheet **5c**).

3. Suggest improvements to your design. Could you use any organic ingredients? Sketch and label your improved design on design sheet **6b**.

4. Explain how and why your design has changed.

On your design sheets

- Record the differences between non-organically and organically grown food. **6a**

- Explain how your design idea can be improved. **6b**

- Record your developed design. **6b**

- Describe how and why you have developed it. **6b**

Remember

- Pesticides are chemicals used in the production of crops.

- Organic foods are produced without the use of chemicals.

Product Development

7

EATING SAFELY

New food products are constantly needed to replace older, existing products. The development of an idea into a new food product can take just a few weeks. Or, it can take years to develop.

Product design

New products may be developed to add to an existing range. These might include a different flavour yoghurt or a new sandwich filling. Such products are regarded as **fast track projects**. The new product may be launched in a matter of weeks.

However, an entirely new product will take a great deal more time. Many people will be involved in the product development team. A great deal of investigating, testing and evaluating will need to be carried out.

Product brief

Usually a food technologist will be given a product brief. This will come from the company requiring the new product. The food technologist may be employed by the company, or they may be recruited specially for the project.

The product brief is the most important aspect of the project. It must be clear and understood by everyone in the product development team. The brief states the product requirements. These will vary depending on the company writing it and the type of product required. Product requirements provided in a brief include:

▷ product type (e.g. cold, savoury, hand-held snack)

▷ target selling price

▷ financial budget

▷ final weight/volume

▷ shelf-life and storage-life

▷ type of packaging

▷ target consumer group

▷ labelling claims

▷ time-scale (to complete project)

▷ connection with existing products (e.g. similar products already on the market).

Existing products

New product development usually begins by looking at the existing product range. This may mean visiting supermarkets, restaurants, take-aways, even other countries! Thorough investigation ensures a completely new product that is acceptable to consumers.

● On task

The company owning 'Anything But The Sandwich' has given you the product brief shown on the right.

1. Develop six ideas to meet the product brief. Present your ideas on design sheet **7a**.

2. Ask others to evaluate your ideas, if possible from the target consumer group. Record their views on design sheet **7b**.

3. Using your consumer evaluation, choose one idea to test. Give reasons for your choice.

4. On design sheet **7c**, produce details of your chosen idea by:

   ► listing ingredients with quantities

   ► describing or sketching the end result

   ► providing information specified in the product brief, including cost.

5. Test your idea by making it and completing an evaluation report for 'Anything But The Sandwich' on design sheet **7d**. Use the product brief on the right to help you.

PRODUCT BRIEF

· Pre-prepared snack product, microwave reheating (if necessary)

· 99p — £1.10

· Individual portion size

· 1 day shelf-life

· Clear plastic packaging, microwaveable (if appropriate)

· Lunchtime, working/business consumers

On your design sheets

● Record your six design ideas. **7a**

● Produce a consumer evaluation. **7b**

● State your chosen idea. Give reasons. **7b**

● Record details of your chosen idea. **7c**

● Present a product evaluation. **7d**

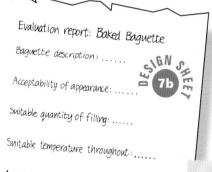

Evaluation report: Baked Baguette

Baguette description: ......

Acceptability of appearance: ......

DESIGN SHEET **7b**

Suitable quantity of filling: ......

Suitable temperature throughout: ......

Acceptability of flavour: ......

Possible product name: ......

Remember

● A product brief states the requirements of a new product to be developed.

Going Green

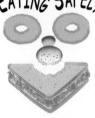

8

EATING SAFELY

Today's consumers are concerned about recycling, wasted energy and excessive packaging. New product design may involve consideration of these 'green' issues.

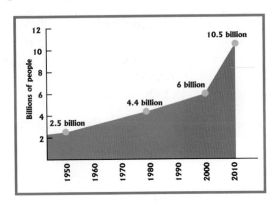

Green issues

The number of people living on our planet is rising.

If the population rises as quickly as estimates predict, we could run out of natural resources. There could be food shortages and a lack of energy. People need to start planning for their planet's future, today.

This is the rather worrying message coming from those who are concerned about **environmental issues**. We use resources in many ways:

▷ electricity is used for lighting and to power household machines and equipment, including computers

▷ rubbish is created because we buy packaged and prepared foods

▷ energy is used to transport, manufacture and process foods

▷ land is used for farming and chemicals may pollute the ground and water

▷ trees are cut down to provide the paper, card and wood we need, often for packaging

▷ animals are reared and slaughtered to feed our growing population.

Green consumers

There are many ways the food industry and its consumers can help today's environment. The more help it gets now, the better the future will be!

Recycle
Most supermarkets and local authorities now provide recycling centres. Glass bottles, aluminium cans, newspapers and some plastics can all be recycled, saving money and natural resources.

Buy loose
Supermarkets and local shops provide a choice of loose fruit, vegetables, bread, etc. This uses less packaging.

On your bike!
Sainsbury's are trying out the Pedicab in Islington. Customers without a car can have their shopping pedalled home. The Pedicab then takes away recycled goods on its return journey.

Energy
Simple things can help save energy, like washing-up rather than using the dishwasher.

Cook!
Consumers can make and cook meals and snacks rather than buy ready-meals or take-aways. This can be fun as well as helping save the environment.

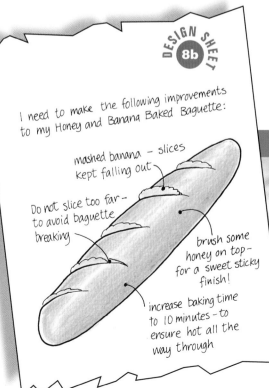

DESIGN SHEET 8b

I need to make the following improvements to my Honey and Banana Baked Baguette:

mashed banana – slices kept falling out

Do not slice too far – to avoid baguette breaking

brush some honey on top – for a sweet sticky finish!

increase baking time to 10 minutes – to ensure hot all the way through

● On task 1
'Anything But The Sandwich' wants to be seen to be green! Working in groups, find out more about environmental issues.

Each group could take one topic to research, for example, recycling, organic farming, renewable energy or food miles. Libraries often have lots of useful information. Use a CD-ROM encyclopedia. Collect leaflets from supermarkets.

Record your findings on design sheet **8a**. Present your investigations to the rest of the class.

● On task 2
Look back at your last design idea for 'Anything But The Sandwich'. On design sheet **8b**:

1. Use your evaluation report to suggest improvements to your design.

2. Make notes about your improvements. Explain why you have made them.

3. Record your final idea. Include ingredients and quantities. Use sketches and colour to show ingredients and textures if appropriate.

4. How will you make your final idea? On design sheet **8c**, list each step of the production. Note any hazards that may occur. State how you will avoid them. Look back at page 107 to help you with this.

On your design sheets
- Record your information about environmental issues. **8a**
- Make notes about your improved idea. **8b**
- Record your final idea. **8b**
- Present a hazard analysis of your final idea. **8c**

Remember
- We have a growing world population.
- As consumers we need to try to help save our environment.

The Final Test

A new food product has been developed for 'Anything But The Sandwich'. It is now time for the final test... and the final evaluation.

Being responsible

Anybody who works in the catering trade or food industry has a responsiblity to their customers. They are responsible for ensuring customers can eat their food safely.

Food workers must ensure high standards of health and safety at each stage of production. Appropriate training must be provided by their manager.

There are many qualifications that food workers can obtain to prove they have studied food hygiene. These qualifications range from a basic food hygiene certificate to degree level courses.

Hygiene must be properly managed. There is a legal responsibility to maintain adequate standards of food hygiene, and to ensure food is fit for consumption.

● On task

Now you have completed your final design, it is time to make and evaluate it.

If possible, swop your design idea and production plan with someone else. Then test their idea for them! You can help them to evaluate the results.

Follow the evaluation steps below:

1. Make your (or your partner's) final design following the production plan. Remember all you have learned about hygiene and safety.

2. While you are working, note any changes that need to be made to the design or production plan. Record these on design sheet **9a**.

3. Now think about hygiene. Either on your own or with your partner, consider the steps you took to be hygienic. Could you make any improvements? Make a note of your ideas on design sheet **9a**.

4. If possible, evaluate your final design straight away. You could work with your partner. You are now going to evaluate the results of your product. On design sheet **9a** you will need to consider the:

▶ appearance (does it look appetising?)

▶ aroma (does it smell appetising?)

▶ taste (how would you describe its taste?)

▶ texture (what does it feel like in the mouth or when you bite it?)

5. Finally, you need to consider how your design can be improved. Again, you could discuss this with a partner.

On design sheet **9b**, show how you could improve your design in the following areas:

▶ production (including method, hygiene points, cooking times, etc.)

▶ ingredients (replace, add or leave out)

▶ how suitable would it be for sale at 'Anything But The Sandwich'?

▶ a consideration of green issues.

Look back at your evaluation notes on design sheet **9a** to help you with this.

Final design: Melted Brie and Grape Croissant

Design and Production notes

• Fresh croissants were difficult to cut neatly – maybe try prepacked croissants next time?

Hygiene notes

• I left the Brie cheese on the side until I needed it. I should have kept it cool in the fridge (1°C – 4°C)

Sensory evaluation

• Appearance – the croissant looks very appetising because it has a lovely golden brown colour and you can see the filling peeping out of the edges

DESIGN SHEET 9a

Final design: Melted Brie and Grape Croissant

• Improvements

Increase amount of Brie and Grape

Quite messy to eat

Better if served in a greaseproof bag

DESIGN SHEET 9b

On your design sheets

● Record your notes made during production. **9a**

● Record your hygiene notes. **9a**

● Describe the sensory evaluation of your final design. **9a**

● Describe any improvements needed. **9b**

Remember

● Anyone preparing food for others has a responsibility to ensure it is safe.

Starting Point

Today you don't have to go to a cake shop or bakers to buy a decorated cake for a special occasion. Many supermarkets sell them on their shelves or they are made to order.

Introduction

Decorated cakes may be large, small or individual ones. Sometimes a catalogue of cake designs is available for the customer to browse through and choose the cake they want. This can even be done using the Internet.

A large supermarket chain is looking for a new company to take over the production of their celebration cakes.

You have been asked to supply six cake designs for a special occasion. You must choose one of your designs to make as a sample cake to take to a meeting with the supermarket's Product Buyer.

A **Product Buyer** is someone who looks at products being made and decides which to buy for sale in their supermarket. As well as looking at the quality of a product, a Product Buyer will have to decide if their customers are likely to want to buy the product.

You will be competing with other companies, all hoping to win the contract with the supermarket. Therefore you must concentrate on the quality of your designing and the quality of your making. Your sample cake must also represent good value for money.

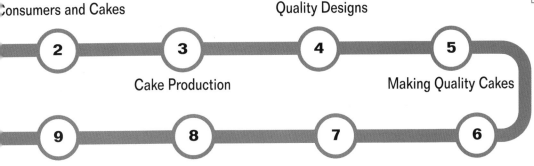

Consumers and Cakes — 2

Cake Production — 3

Quality Designs — 4

Making Quality Cakes — 5

6 — Comparing Cakes

7 — A Nice Ice

8 — An Interview with... Jane Asher

9 — Storing Cakes

Fresh ideas. Party Cakes

The focus

In this unit you will focus on the production of cakes. This will include different methods used. It will also involve learning about the functions of different ingredients in cakes. You will find out about the various icings used for different cakes.

You will also focus on quality designing and making. You will need to find out how to produce quality products by carefully planning their production.

The challenge

During this challenge you need to find inspiration for your new cake design ideas. You must investigate by looking at existing products and carrying out comparisons. You will need to test different recipes in order to develop your own new product. You will be testing the ingredients and the production method.

The production system you set up must include quality control checks. Then you will evaluate the results.

The end product

After making your cake for the final time you may display the result. You can then compare your cakes as a class. This will help you consider ways you might improve your cake if you were to make it again.

Your cake must also be presented to the supermarket Product Buyer. Their comments will form part of your evaluation.

Investigating Cakes

There are numerous different cakes on sale today. Some are suitable as a quick snack. Others are fit for a celebration. To design a quality cake you need to investigate what is already available.

Cake shops

Specialist cake shops, such as Jane Asher's Party Cakes, make and sell cakes. There are very few shops that specialise only in cakes. The advantage is that they can make a cake to suit a particular consumer. Making cakes in this way is known as **one-off production**.

Cakes can also be bought from bakery shops. Most of these will be made in the bakery or on the shop premises. They are made on a **small scale** usually in batches. This is known as **batch production**.

Supermarkets sell lots of cakes. They can be found on the shelves, in freezer or chill cabinets and sometimes at an in-store bakery. Apart from the 'made-to-order' celebratory cakes, these cakes are **mass produced**. This means a number of identical cakes are made all the time for a certain length of time, such as Mr Kipling's cakes.

● On task 1

1. Work with a partner. Brainstorm all the different types of cake you can remember. Where might they be sold?

   Record your ideas as a diagram on design sheet **1a**.

2. With your partner, brainstorm occasions that might require a special cake to be made. Record these also on design sheet **1a**.

3. Try to visit shops that sell cakes. Add more ideas to your diagram when you can.

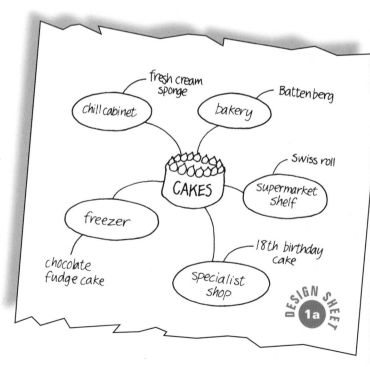

Making comparisons

Food products and equipment are often tested by magazines and newspapers. The *Good Food* magazine might compare different mincepies at Christmas, or ice creams in the summer. This can help consumers decide what to buy.

On the right is an example of a comparison carried out by a newspaper. Eight mass-produced celebratory cakes were compared. The results provide a description of the flavour, appearance and texture of the cakes. The article also gives an opinion of each cake – what is good about it, and what is disappointing. Finally the cakes are awarded a number of stars – the more stars, the better value the product.

CONSUMING INTERESTS: BIRTHDAY CAKES

THE EXCITEMENT of commercial birthday cakes has always, no doubt, been more do with their appearance than how good they are to eat. Still, it was disappointing to find just how little supermarkets care what their cakes taste like nowadays.

Once sliced, most of those we tried were sugary but dull, dull, dull – and some were anything but a treat to eat. There was only one, predictably expensive, cake that I would want to see at any birthday celebration of my own.

Sainsbury's Seriously Chocolatey Birthday cake,
£4.75 (no weight stated)
Claims: "A moist rich chocolate cake with a chocolate butter-cream filling topped with chocolate-fudge icing, decorated with a milk chocolate plaque. Serves 10."
Verdict" Our Happy Birthday plaque developed an ominous crack. For chocoholic teenagers only. Most testers found it dreary.
★

Harvey Nichols Birthday cake,
£29.95 for 3lb
Claims: "Fresh seasonal fruit and sponge."
Verdict: A magnificent eye-catcher, a sort of giant charlotte topped with fresh fruit in seven varieties, decoratively arranged. The Happy Birthday message was discreetly inscribed on a chocolate wafer. Best of all, the filling was up to scratch: four fine layers of sponge separating thick layers of a delectable patisserie cream. Very impressive.
★ ★ ★ ★ ★

Somerfield Chocolate Birthday Cake,
£3.99 (no weight stated)
Claims: "Chocolate madeira filled with chocolate butter-cream, topped with plain chocolate icing. Eight servings."
Verdict: This was preferred to the Sainsbury's offering for appearance and taste. It was lighter and moister in texture, and though it did not look exciting recipients came back for more.
★ ★

● *On task 2*

1. Work together as a class to carry out a comparison test. Use cakes or another food product provided by your teacher. Use the approach shown above. Record your results on design sheet **1b**.

2. Choose a 'special occasions' theme for your cake. For example, Birthday, Halloween, Bonfire night, etc. Make a collection of pictures to do with your theme from magazines and leaflets. Think about colours, textures, shapes and patterns as well as objects. Present your pictures on design sheet **1c**.

Images on the theme of a teenage birthday:

DESIGN SHEET **1c**

On your design sheets

- Record different types of cake and where they are sold. **1a**

- List special occasions that might require a cake. **1a**

- Present the results of your product comparison test. **1b**

- Present your collection of theme pictures. **1c**

Remember

- Many food products can be made as 'one-offs', in batches or they can be mass produced.

- Comparison tests can be helpful to consumers when choosing food products.

Consumers and Cakes

There are many types of cake. There are many more types of consumer! When designing a new cake, the needs of the consumer must be met.

Consumer needs

The cakes shown on the right have each been designed and made for a particular person. They are also for special occasions.

Cakes are not always designed so specifically. However, the needs of the consumer are always important. The sort of needs a consumer might have include:

Dietary	Lifestyle
low fat	busy working
allergies	elderly
diabetic	low income
healthy	high income
high NSP	young children
low salt	love cooking
vegetarian	hate cooking

When designing a quality cake it is important to find out the needs of your consumer.

● **On task 1**

Imagine someone is going to make a birthday cake specially for you.

1. On design sheet **2a**, list all the dietary needs that are special to you. Think about the ingredients you can't eat, or don't like at all. For example, are you a vegetarian, do you like fresh cream, or marzipan?

2. Compare your list with someone in your class. The list will probably be different. This is why it is important to know the needs of your consumer when designing new products. Record your comparison on design sheet **2a**.

What makes a cake?

A cake is a food product that is baked and tastes sweet. Its texture depends on the ingredients it contains. It could be moist, light, soft, chewy, dry or crumbly. It is usually eaten by itself and it is sometimes eaten as a dessert. Cakes can be filled, iced, decorated, shaped, covered and layered.

Categories of cakes

Cakes can be put into groups. The simplest groups to use are the methods of making cakes. There is more about cake production on the next page. These methods are the ones traditionally used at home. Some examples are shown on the right.

● On task 2

1. Working in groups, investigate the different methods of making cakes.

2. Test the method your teacher gives you by making a small batch of cakes. Compare the results by looking at the:

- ▶ method
- ▶ time for making
- ▶ ease of making
- ▶ time for baking
- ▶ appearance
- ▶ texture
- ▶ flavour

Your teacher may photocopy samples to show the texture produced by each method.

Produce a results table and write down your conclusions on design sheet **2b**.

Creaming

Fat and sugar creamed together; eggs beaten in; flour folded in

or

All-in-one method

All ingredients beaten together

Rubbing-in

Fat rubbed into flour; sugar and flavourings added; eggs/milk added to bind

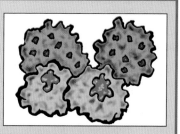

Melting

Fat melted with syrup/sugar/treacle; dry ingredients added

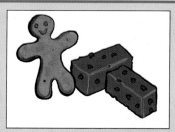

Whisking

Eggs and sugar whisked together; flour folded in

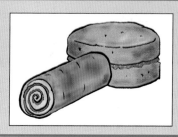

On your design sheets

- ● Record your list of needs for your own birthday cake. **2a**

- ● Compare your list with someone else's. **2a**

- ● Record the results of your investigation into different cake methods. **2b**

- ● Write a conclusion to your investigation. **2b**

Remember

- ● Consumer needs must be taken into account when designing new food products.

- ● Four traditional methods of making cakes are creaming, rubbing in, whisking and melting.

Cake Production

Before designing a quality cake it is important to know how cakes are made. There are various methods. This is why there are so many different types of cake.

Lots of cakes

When food manufacturers make cakes on a large scale they may use similar methods to the traditional ones. Of course, the quantities and the machinery used are much larger. Sometimes different ingredients are added to improve the quality of large-scale cakes:

▷ salt may be used to bring out the flavour

▷ water may be added to create steam during baking

▷ preservatives may be used to help cakes last longer

▷ **emulsifiers** may be added to stop the fat or oil from separating

▷ glycerine (a thick sweet liquid) may be added for moisture.

The flow chart on the right shows the production of chocolate cakes. It has been divided into four areas:

Input   everything that goes into the system

Process   everything that happens to the input

Output   the finished product

Feedback information needed to be passed back down the system

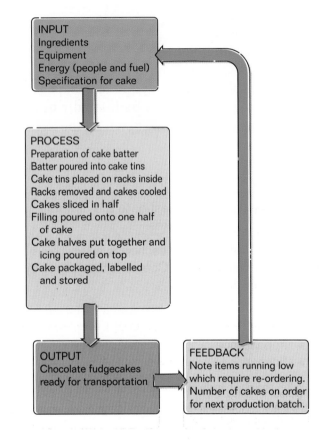

INPUT
Ingredients
Equipment
Energy (people and fuel)
Specification for cake

PROCESS
Preparation of cake batter
Batter poured into cake tins
Cake tins placed on racks inside
Racks removed and cakes cooled
Cakes sliced in half
Filling poured onto one half
  of cake
Cake halves put together and
  icing poured on top
Cake packaged, labelled
  and stored

OUTPUT
Chocolate fudgecakes
ready for transportation

FEEDBACK
Note items running low
which require re-ordering.
Number of cakes on order
for next production batch.

Testing times

In the food industry ovens are often computerised so the cooking time and temperature are always the same.

When testing cakes on a small scale the cooking time on the recipe is only a guide. So you need to know how to test if a cake is cooked.

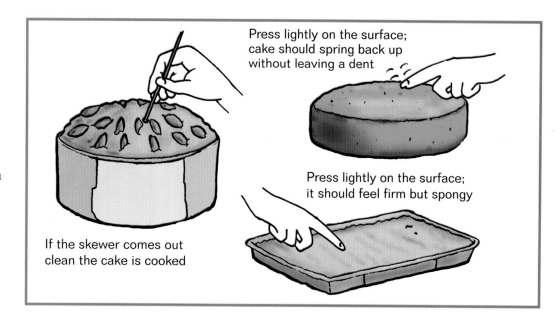

Press lightly on the surface; cake should spring back up without leaving a dent

If the skewer comes out clean the cake is cooked

Press lightly on the surface; it should feel firm but spongy

● On task

Choose one of the cake recipes provided by your teacher. On your design sheet produce your own flow chart or system to show the production of that cake.

Remember, you will need to break the process down into simple stages. Use the headings input, process, output and feedback.

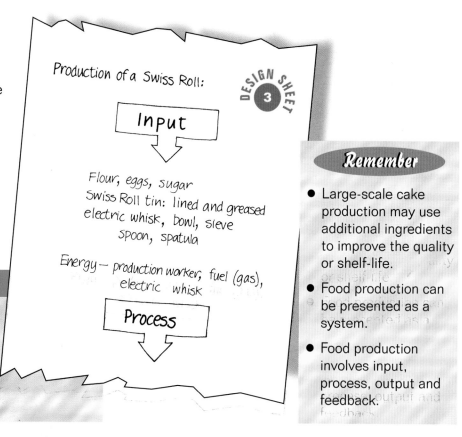

Production of a Swiss Roll:

DESIGN SHEET 3

Input

Flour, eggs, sugar
Swiss Roll tin: lined and greased
electric whisk, bowl, sieve
spoon, spatula

Energy — production worker, fuel (gas), electric whisk

Process

On your design sheet

- Present your production system of a cake recipe.

Remember

- Large-scale cake production may use additional ingredients to improve the quality or shelf-life.
- Food production can be presented as a system.
- Food production involves input, process, output and feedback.

Quality Designs

4

Quality cakes cannot be manufactured unless quality cakes have been designed. A quality design will be one that meets all the needs of the consumer.

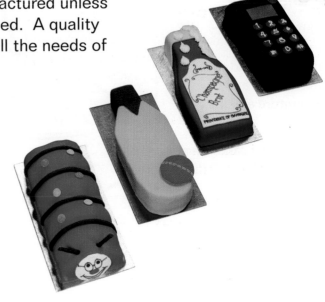

Target consumer groups

When designing a new food product it is essential to find out exactly what the consumer wants. This is usually carried out using market research. Consumers from a target group (such as mothers with young children) are asked questions about what they buy. They may also be asked their opinion of products currently on sale.

When designing a food product such as a cake, the following must be taken into account:

▷ the needs of the target consumer group

▷ how those needs can be met.

Consumer needs can be met by considering the following things:

▷ the best ingredients, materials and equipment

▷ the most suitable style/shape/design

▷ how user-friendly (to open/prepare/cook/eat)

▷ the most suitable packaging

▷ clear and accurate labelling

▷ its effect on the environment

▷ good value for money.

● *On task 1*

The quality of a product's design may be judged without actually looking at the way it has been made.

Look at the food packet shown above, or use one supplied by your teacher. Use the questions below to help make a judgement about the quality of design of the product.

Record your investigation on design sheet **4a**.

QUALITY OF DESIGN

1. Which target consumer group is this product aimed at?

2. How suitable is the style/shape/design for those consumers?

3. Taking into account the ingredients, how well do you think the needs of the consumers are met?

4. Does the product appear to be user-friendly (to open, to eat, etc.)?

5. Is the labelling clear?

6. How might this product's packaging affect the environment?

Presenting designs

A quality cake design needs a quality presentation! There are many ways to present designs and there are also many design ideas for each new product.

A food product idea may start as a rough sketch, perhaps with a few labels.

As the idea develops so the design will include more and more detail.

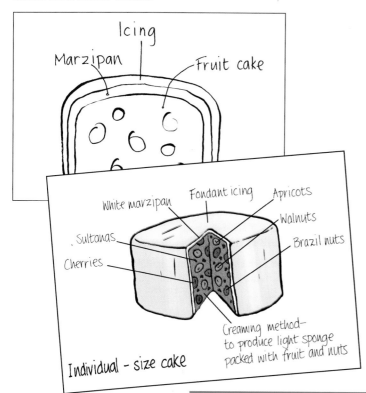

Design ideas may be presented using a computer drawing program. They can also be presented as a recipe with diagrams showing any detailed decoration, garnish, pattern, shape, layering, etc.

● On task 2

1. You have been asked to supply six designs of cakes for a special occasion. Which special occasion have you chosen? Which target consumer group will you be aiming at? You will need to carry out market research to find out the needs of your consumer group. Record your choices on design sheet **4a**.

2. Outline your ideas for cake designs on design sheet **4b**. Use notes, sketches, colour and tone. Remember to use your collection of pictures and leaflets and the results of your investigation to help you. Explain which method of cake making you will choose.

3. Choose one design idea that you like. Develop it further on design sheet **4c** by including more detail. List the ingredients. Describe or show the texture and appearance of the cake.

4. Test your idea by making it. Describe your success on design sheet **4d**. Note any changes needed.

Test idea: Nutty Fruit Cake

When testing my sample Nutty Fruit Cake I found the mixture difficult to mix because I had quite large pieces of fruit and nuts.

Next time I will chop the nuts and apricots to make them smaller.

I will keep the cherry halves the same as I think they look attractive when the cake is cut.

DESIGN SHEET 9d

On your design sheets

- Record your investigation into the quality of design. **4a**

- Record your chosen special occasion and target consumer group. **4b**

- Present six initial designs. **4b**

- Develop one idea in more detail. **4c**

- Describe the success of your first test idea. **4d**

- Explain any changes you need to make. **4d**

Remember

- Research into consumer needs can be carried out using market research.

- Design ideas can be presented (or communicated) in many ways.

Making Quality Cakes

5

A quality cake is one which is always the same. It does not change its standard of quality. The food manufacturer has to decide on that standard.

Quality making

In order to design quality cakes it is first necessary to look at making quality cakes. High quality cakes are manufactured using a process of **quality assurance**. Quality assurance is a system that ensures a product will be of a specific quality. It does this through quality control.

Quality control

Quality assurance is achieved through **quality control checks**. These checks occur at every stage of making the product. Quality control ensures that problems do not arise during manufacture.

Look back through the previous unit to remind yourself about hazards.

HACCP

HACCP stands for **Hazard Analysis Critical Control Points**. It is a quality assurance system used in food manufacture. HACCP works by:

▷ looking at every step of the production carefully
▷ identifying where problems might occur
▷ deciding on a quality control check to prevent the problem
▷ checking the quality control checks work.

Below is an example of quality assurance using HACCP.

Production of sandwich cake has been studied and possible problems identified (in brackets). Quality checks agreed (then checked).

	Quality control checks

Input
Ingredients/equipment/energy/specification
(stock out of date or going off, equipment
old or likely to break, weighing scales
not accurate)
	* check stock rotation
	  (older items used first)
	* check temperature of store rooms
	  (cold storage)
	* check equipment is in good working order

Process 1. Beat all ingredients together (cakes with different textures)	* time beating of ingredients
2. Pour into greased tins (some cakes larger than others)	* control amount of cake mixture in tins

3. Bake
   (uneven baking or burnt)
	* control oven times, shelf position and
	  temperatures

4. Remove from oven and tin	
5. Cool (packaged when warm)	* control cooling times
6. Spread with jam; place together (jam spilling out of middle)	* measure amount of jam in filling
7. Dust with icing sugar (uneven icing sugar)	* control dusting of icing sugar
8. Package, label and store	* check packaging and best-before dates
Output Jam sandwich cake	

During production samples are checked to ensure that they are the correct weight

● On task

Work with a partner. Choose a cake recipe that both of you would like to test.

1. Look carefully at the production and identify where problems could arise. Suggest quality control checks that would prevent the problems.

2. Present your production plan as input, process and output on design sheet **5a**. Add quality control checks. Note the things you have already learnt about cake making that will help you test your recipe.

3. Both test your chosen recipe following your production plan. Make sure you carry out the quality control checks.

4. The products made by you and your partner should be of the same quality. Compare your results. Record your results on design sheet **5b**.

DESIGN SHEET 5a

Production plan for a Swiss Roll:

Input	Quality control checks
Flour, sugar	(older products used first) • check stock rotation
Eggs	(store at 5°C / use-by date) • check temperature of fridge and use-by date
Swiss Roll tin	(size important for correct cooking) • 27cm x 18cm tin
Lined and greased	(sponge may stick) • greaseproof paper, greased
Electric whisk, bowl, sieve, spoon, spatula	(correct working order and clean) • check all equipment
Energy	(avoid over/under cooking) • gas mark 7

Process

On your design sheets

- Record your production plan with quality control checks. **5a**

- Make notes about what you have learnt about cake making.

- Present the results of your quality comparison. **5b**

Remember

- Quality assurance is is a system that ensures products are of a specific quality.

- Quality assurance is achieved through quality control checks.

- HACCP is a quality assurance system often used in the food industry.

Comparing Cakes

6

When a consumer wants a cake there is a choice – buy the ingredients and make it, use a packet mix, or buy one ready-made. But how do these cakes compare? What is the quality of the results?

Making comparisons

Comparing cakes should involve more than just their taste, texture and appearance. A comparison can be made of the cost, portion size and the time and effort involved in making them.

Look at the ingredients listed below. One list is from a recipe for shortcakes. The other is from shop-bought shortcakes.

On the right is an outline of the function of each ingredient used to make homemade shortcakes.

Home-made Strawberry Shortcakes	Shop-bought Strawberry Shortcakes
self-raising flour butter sugar milk egg strawberry jam double cream	wheatflour butter sugar strawberry jam (with pectin, malic acid, acidity regulator, sodium citrate) glucose syrup modified corn starch flavourings dried egg white

INGREDIENT	FUNCTION/ROLE IN ROCK CAKES
Self-raising flour	• adds 'bulk' or structure to the cakes • contains baking powder which helps the cakes to rise • helps cakes turn golden brown
Fat (butter or margarine)	• adds flavour • coats flour during rubbing-in to make a crumbly ('short') texture
Sugar (caster or) granulated	• adds sweetness • helps delay staling • adds to the colour
Milk (whole, skimmed or semi-skimmed)	• helps bind dry ingredients together • contains protein which helps cakes to 'set' (coagulate)
Egg	• helps bind dry ingredients together • contains protein that helps cakes to 'set'

Added extras

Shop-bought shortcakes have added ingredients. Here are some reasons why they are used:

Pectin (E440) Malic acid (E296)	Gelling agents that help the jam to set
Acidity regulator Sodium citrate	Keeps a constant acid level and adds flavour
Glucose syrup	Liquid form of sugar; easier to use in large quantities
Modified corn Starch	Cornflour that has been treated, allowing it to thicken liquids
Flavourings	Add extra flavour
Dried egg white	Easier to handle and store

DESIGN SHEET 6b

sensory evaluation results

Triangle Test 1

☀ = homemade

○ = shop bought   ☐ = packet-mix

Taster 1 ☐	☀	○	☐
How would you rate the appearance?	9	6	8
How would you rate the flavour?	8	2	6
Which do you think was shop-bought?		✓	
Which did you prefer?	✓		

Function of ingredients

Every ingredient plays a special role in the manufacture of a food product. Sometimes one item can be changed for something else. For example, changing walnuts to hazelnuts, or sultanas to raisins.

The main ingredients cannot always be changed because of the function they perform. This can lead to a conflict of demands between designing and making a product.

It is important to know the function of the different ingredients chosen when designing new food products.

● On task

1. In groups, choose a cake product to compare. It must be one that can be homemade, bought as a packet-mix and ready-made.

2. Make the homemade and packet-mix products. On design sheet **6a**, note the time taken to prepare and cook each one. Also note the number of items of equipment used. Comment on whether they were easy or difficult to make.

3. Evaluate the results using a sensory taste test. You could set up a triangle test. Ask tasters if they can tell which one is homemade.

4. Decide how best to present your results (spreadsheets, graphs, charts, written report or a combination). Record your results on design sheet **6b**.

5. In your opinion, which is the best quality cake? Explain your reasons on design sheet **6b**.

On your design sheets

- Describe your comparative investigation. **6a**
- Present the results of your sensory evaluation. **6b**
- Explain your conclusions. **6b**

Remember

- Ingredients have special functions in food manufacture.
- When designing food products it is important to know the function of each ingredient.

A Nice Ice

A quality cake needs a quality finish! What type of icing will be on top of your cake? There are many to choose from...

Types of icing

The type of icing chosen often depends on the type of cake. A chocolate cake, for example, might have chocolate icing. A fruit cake might have a layer of marzipan and royal icing. These are mostly traditional ways of decorating cakes.

Today many icings can be bought ready-made. Sometimes this saves a lot of time and effort. For example, fondant icing is time-consuming to make and involves boiling sugar. Other icings are easy to make and can be varied in their colour, flavour and consistency. Below are some popular types of icing.

Glacé icing

A runny icing that can be poured over fairy cakes or sponges. Made from icing sugar and warm water (or lemon/orange juice).

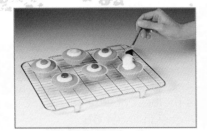

Almond paste (marzipan)

A soft paste often used as a layer between cake and icing on fruit cakes. Made from ground almonds, sugar and eggs. It can be white or yellow (with colouring added).

Royal icing

A special icing used over marzipan to coat fruit cakes. It is put on in layers, which must dry hard between coats. It helps to preserve the cake. Made from icing sugar and egg white.

Fondant icing

A soft paste that can be rolled out and used to cover fruit or Madeira cakes. It can also be moulded into shapes and figures. Made from sugar, water and liquid glucose.

Buttercream

A spreadable icing used on top or inside sponge cakes. It can also be piped. Made from butter and icing sugar. It can be flavoured with fruit juice, chocolate, nuts, etc.

Chocolate fudge icing

A rich, spreadable icing used on the top, sides and middle of chocolate fudge cakes. Made from sugar, milk, chocolate, butter and cream (recipes vary).

Icing ideas

Some more ideas for icings, fillings and decorations include: jam, apricot glaze, fruits, nuts, melted chocolate, fresh cream, lemon curd, chocolate leaves or curls.

The type of icing and filling chosen should enhance and compliment a cake

● On task

1. Choose the type of icing(s) you would like to use. Explain your choice on design sheet **7a**.

2. Develop your design idea on design sheet **7a**. Use the information in **An Interview with** Jane Asher on pages 131–2 to help you. Include details of your decoration, icing and filling. Remember to include any improvements from your previous testing. Add ingredients with quantities to your design.

3. Test your developed idea. In particular, you will need to test your choice of icing. Show how you did this on design sheet **7b**.

4. Record the success of your developed idea on design sheet **7b**.

On your design sheets

- State your choice of icing, with reasons. **7a**

- Present your developed idea, including ingredients and quantities. **7a**

- Show how you tested your developed idea. **7b**

- Describe the success of your developed idea after testing it. **7b**

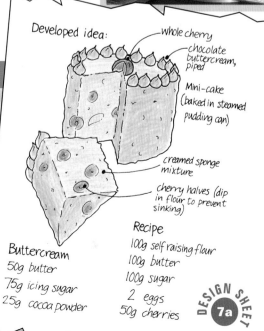

Developed idea:

whole cherry

chocolate buttercream, piped

Mini-cake (baked in steamed pudding can)

creamed sponge mixture

cherry halves (dip in flour to prevent sinking)

Buttercream
50g butter
75g icing sugar
25g cocoa powder

Recipe
100g self raising flour
100g butter
100g sugar
2 eggs
50g cherries

DESIGN SHEET **7a**

Remember

- A variety of icings are available to make or buy.

- The icing should enhance and improve a cake.

8

An Interview with... Jane Asher

A CAKE of QUALITY

Jane Asher's Party Cakes shop is in the heart of Chelsea in London. The shop specialises in making quality celebration cakes for all occasions. The cakes are chosen by the customers and designs include spaceships, pigs and a pair of lips!

PARTY CAKES

At Jane Asher's Party Cakes shop a customer can look through a portfolio containing over two and a half thousand designs.

Just four people are employed to make and decorate between 40 and 50 cakes a week.

Individually handcrafted cakes like these are made exactly to the customer's request. They choose the shape, size and design. They can even state special dietary requirements.

The cakes may be rich fruit or flavoured sponges – chocolate, vanilla, lemon or carrot cake. A fruit cake will be made between four and six months before it is decorated.

To make a novelty cake, the design will be shaped out of a large cake. Moulds are not used as these limit the shapes and designs.

Models are shaped out of coloured fondant icing. Flowers are piped in royal icing. Flowers are very time consuming so they are started before the cake is even made! One person will make and decorate a cake from start to finish. Just like handwriting, everyone has their own style of cake decorating.

All ingredients are fresh – butter, farm fresh eggs – and the alcohol is real! Preservatives are not used.

On your design sheet

- Work out the cost of your developed cake idea.

Can you describe your business?

" Jane Asher's Party Cakes started in 1991. We design and make quality celebration cakes for all occasions. The cakes are specially commissioned and handmade for the customer. In the cake market they are the equivalent of fashion's 'haute couture'! "

Where do you get your ideas and inspiration for cake designs?

" From the customer! Sometimes the customer knows exactly what they want. They tell us in detail how their cake should look. Others just need to go through our cake design catalogues to find something they like.

Occasionally a customer has no idea so we ask about the person who will receive the cake; their hobbies, interests, personality and so on. For example, one lady could not think of a suitable cake design for her elderly mother until she mentioned her mother's name was Daisy. We created a cake covered in daisies!

Of course it is also important to keep up to date and have fresh ideas. Talking to my children helps with this. New ideas are not usually a problem, although there are occasions like Christmas where (almost) everything has been done already. "

How do you find out what consumers want?

" Unlike the cakes I design for Sainsbury's, my customers actually tell me what they want. They look at my designs and choose one of those or something similar. If it doesn't exactly fit their requirements then we come up with a design that does. It is important to look at trends and listen to people.

Sainsbury's carry out a lot of research with 'focus groups' so they can predict what will be popular in the future. However, I also feel people do not always know what they want until they see it! "

What sort of things do you do to ensure you produce quality cakes?

" Quality cakes must start with quality ingredients. We only use the best, freshest ingredients. It is like building a house – if the foundations are not strong it will fall down!

The staff are also of a high standard. They are well trained.

To sum up – we use the best quality we can in each area of the production and keep tight control on everything that happens. "

What advice would you give to someone designing and making a cake for a special celebration?

" I would say, use the best ingredients you can get and don't be too ambitious! Be clean, neat and tidy when you are working.

Also, it is important to test your ideas. Try out ideas to see if they work then improve or simplify the design. Practise the skills you will need. Know your limitations and explore your talents. If you are good at modelling use that rather than try to pipe a decoration! Fresh flowers can make an attractive looking cake if you can't manage other decorative methods.

Consider the person who will receive the cake. It must be right for the occasion and right for the person. Then it will be really appreciated! "

Storing Cakes

9

A cake of quality must be packaged and stored to keep it in perfect condition. But the packaging must be chosen carefully. It must not harm the cake, or the environment.

Keeping qualities

Different types of cake will keep for different lengths of time. This is due to the ingredients they contain.

A rich fruit cake has a high sugar and fat content and will keep for months. A tier from a wedding cake can keep for years if it is properly iced. (Traditionally it was kept for the first Christening.)

A swiss roll, on the other hand, does not contain any fat which means it becomes dry quickly. A home-made swiss roll is at its best the day it is made.

Preservatives

Cakes bought in the shops often have preservatives added to them. These give the cakes a longer shelf-life by improving their keeping qualities. In other words, they stop the cakes going stale as quickly as they would normally. E numbers beginning with 2 are preservatives. E202 is sometimes added to cakes. Its name is potassium sorbate.

Storing cakes at home

At home cakes are often kept in airtight containers. Air will dry out a cake causing it to become stale. The more fat in a cake, the longer it will keep.

A cake high in sugar (including fruit) may become mouldy if it is kept in warm conditions. Bacteria feed on the sugar and they will multiply quickly, even in a container.

Packaging cakes for shops

Celebration cakes from specialist shops or supermarkets usually come in cardboard boxes. These may be plain or display the manufacturer's logo.

Cakes sold from chill cabinets also come in cardboard boxes. These sometimes have a cellophane top so the consumer can see the product. A frozen cake requires a stronger card packaging and may also have a plastic container inside to protect it.

Ambient cakes

The sort of cakes found on supermarket shelves are known as **ambient**. This means they are stored at room temperature. They have a longer shelf-life than chilled or fresh cakes.

The type of packaging used might be a heat-sealed plastic bag inside a cardboard box. The box will be designed to attract the consumer's eye as well as protect the contents.

Cadbury LAND

FUDGE Cakes

Chocolate sponge cakes topped with delicious Cadbury's Fudge and covered with Cadbury's Milk Chocolate.

INGREDIENTS: Milk Chocolate (36%) [Sugar, Cocoa Mass, Cocoa Butter, Skimmed Milk Powder, Milk Fat, Vegetable Fat, Whey Powder, Emulsifier (E322)], Sugar, Glucose Syrup, Wheatflour, Sweetened Condensed Milk, Hydrogenated Vegetable Oil, Humectant (Vegetable Glycerine), Butter Oil, Fat-Reduced Cocoa, Dried Whole Egg, Soya Flour, Lactose, Emulsifiers (E322, E471, E475), Salt, Flavouring, Milk Protein, Preservative (Potassium Sorbate).

SUITABLE FOR VEGETARIANS

Environmental issues

Packaging has a number of important functions. It:

▷ protects the contents from damage

▷ maintains hygiene

▷ allows easy stacking and storage

▷ helps identify the product

▷ carries information (labelling)

▷ sells the product (by being eye-catching).

However, all this packaging is creating a great deal of waste. The more packaging that can be recycled, the better for the environment. Look back at Unit 5 as a reminder about environmental issues.

Paper and board

Cardboard and paper are made from the raw ingredients cellulose and wood pulp. Paper and cardboard packaging must be recycled rather than thrown away. If recycled they can be used as raw material and made into more paper and cardboard. The diagram below shows the recycling process:

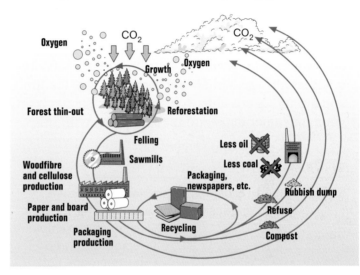

● On task

1. What sort of packaging will your cake require? Show your ideas on design sheet **9a**. What shelf-life will it have?

2. Plan a production system for your cake on design sheet **9b**. Include quality control checks.

3. Finalise your cake design and make it.

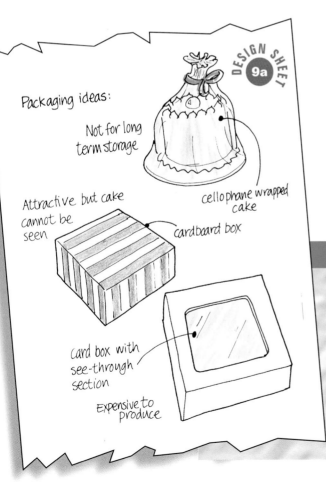

DESIGN SHEET 9a

Packaging ideas:

Not for long term storage

cellophane wrapped cake

Attractive but cake cannot be seen

cardboard box

card box with see-through section

Expensive to produce

On your design sheets

● Present your ideas for packaging materials and design. **9a**

● State the shelf-life of your final design. **9a**

● Show a production system for your cake, including quality control checks. **9b**

Remember

● Preservatives are sometimes added to cakes to give them a longer shelf-life.

● Correct storage conditions help keep cakes fresh.

● Recycling packaging is better for the environment.

The Final Cake

10

Finally, you need to present six designs and a sample cake to the Product Buyer. The Product Buyer must decide who will supply celebration cakes for the supermarket. How can you convince the Buyer that your products are the best?

Sensory testing

First you need to evaluate your final cake's sensory qualities. These include appearance, taste, texture and aroma. If possible, you should ask people from your consumer target group to help you with this.

● On task 1

1. Draw a large 8-point star profile for your cake. Use characteristics that you would prefer for your cake. For example, lemon-flavoured buttercream, soft sponge, light texture, equal-sized layers, neat decoration, etc.

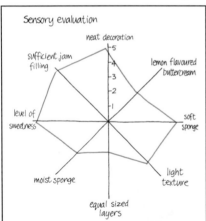

2. Ask your tasters to complete the star profile as they evaluate the sensory characteristics of your cake. Each taster should use a different colour pen so you can evaluate the results easily.

3. Analyse the results from your star profile. Which aspects need improving? How might you improve them? Record the results and improvements on design sheet **10a**.

4. Look back at your production system. How useful was it during the making of your final product? Does it need any adaptations or improvements? Record your changes on design sheet **10a**.

The Asda difference?

This system of evaluation is adapted from one used by Asda. After developing a new product they compare it with similar products made by their competitors. It is a blind-testing. This means the tasters do not know whose product they are tasting.

Using the results from the tasting, Asda give the new product a card:

▶ A red card means the product is unacceptable.

▶ An orange card means the product is only average and the manufacturer has three months to improve it.

▶ A green card means the product is excellent.

This product is not worth buying or developing.

This product is good but it needs further development or improvement

This product is brilliant. I would definitely buy this.

● On task 2

1. If there is time, you could set up your own card system to evaluate the cakes produced by the class. You could evaluate the cakes on their appearance only. Your card system could be based on the colours from traffic lights or cards used in football matches. Ask a number of people to evaluate the cakes using the cards.

2. Finally, prepare a report on your designs and sample cake for the Product Buyer (design sheet **10b**). You will need to convince the Buyer that you have investigated and tested your idea very thoroughly. Include the following details in your report:

▶ your investigation into cakes

▶ your six cake designs

▶ the results of your sensory evaluation

▶ your production system, with suggested improvements

▶ the costing of your final cake

▶ your own evaluation of how well you have worked during this Unit.

DESIGN SHEET 10a

Improvements to the production system

My production system was very easy to follow and helped me to be organised during the production of my cake.

However, I need to make the following adjustment to the 'processes' aspect:

• increase cooling time for the cake. This is because I started to ice the cake before it was properly cold.

On your design sheets

● Present the results of your evaluation. **10a**

● Suggest improvements in your production system. **10a**

● Produce a final report. **10b**

Remember

● The consumer target group must be involved in the evaluation of a new product.

Food Technology Dictionary

Aesthetics

Aesthetics is about how people respond to things through their senses. What we see, hear, taste, touch and smell can be pleasant or unpleasant experiences.

When designing a food product it is important to realise that different people like and dislike different things. Generally, however, people respond well to things which are harmonious (i.e. go together well), or provide contrast (i.e. are opposites).

Analysis

If you are asked to analyse something you will need to break it down into smaller, more detailed parts. So, for example, if you were analysing a ready-made, chilled curry and rice meal, you would need to describe the ingredients, portion size, appearance, container, etc.

Alternatively, you might have been asked to analyse a problem such as providing a suitable meal for a vegetarian. In this case you would have to identify the nutrients required and find out which foods provide those nutrients.

See also **Product analysis**.

Ambient

This refers to a temperature. Ambient foods are those which can be stored at room temperature. They are found on supermarket shelves rather than in special cabinets like freezers.

Coagulate

This term is used to describe the setting of protein during heating. In a project you might make a flan containing eggs. While cooking, the protein in the eggs will set, turning the liquid into a solid. Any food product containing protein will coagulate when heated.

Conflicting demands

When designing, most decisions involve making *compromises*. For example, buttermilk may produce a light texture soda bread but if you cannot easily get hold of buttermilk, it may have to be replaced with milk or yoghurt. In order to give a product a long **shelf-life**, it may need extra or special packaging which could be expensive and might cause environmental damage. You will need to make decisions about these sort of issues.

Is all this packaging really necessary?

Constraints

Constraints are things that limit the possibilities of your design. For example, there may be certain portion sizes, weights, volumes or types of ingredients that you cannot use or, possibly, have been told you cannot use. These constraints may form part of a design specification.

See also **Specification**.

Consumers

Consumers are the people who will eventually use the products you are designing. Remember that consumers have a choice. If they don't like what you have designed, they won't buy it. The particular group of consumers your product is aimed at is sometimes called the *target market* or *target group*.

As you design and develop your product you must keep in mind what consumers need (physically) and want (emotionally). Your product must be safe for them to eat and satisfy all their needs.

Cross-contamination

This comes into *food safety* and *hygiene*. One food can be contaminated with the bacteria from another food if standards of hygiene are poor. For example, separate chopping boards should be used for preparing different types of food.

Decay

As soon as any plant is picked or harvested it starts to decay. This is a natural process which causes the food to spoil. For example, fruit goes brown, loses its moisture and shrinks. This process of decay can be slowed down or temporarily stopped by preservation methods such as freezing, canning, drying and jam-making.

Date marking

Food products will have one of the following date-marks:

► *Use by*: this is for food with a short shelf-life which is likely to go off quickly.

► *Best before*: this is for foods with a longer shelf-life which may not be at their best after this date.

Emulsifier

Emulsifiers are used in the production of food to ensure mixtures remain together. For example, oil and water will separate after they have been mixed together. An emulsifier will stop this separation. Lecithin is a natural emulsifier found in egg yolk, so products like mayonnaise (made from eggs) will not separate out.

Enzymes

Enzymes are natural chemicals found in food. They are not harmful but they do speed up the process of decay. Enzymes are responsible for food such as fruit and vegetables turning brown. It is the enzymes that have to be destroyed when preserving food.

Feedback

This refers to information being passed along a system. It is necessary to ensure the system runs in a controlled way. Feedback might include information like checking to see if a product is cooked. If it takes longer than planned, the system may need to be altered for the future.

Fermentation

This is a process used in the production of bread, wine, beer and in pickling. It usually causes a gas to be produced. For example, in breadmaking yeast ferments with sugar to produce carbon dioxide (a gas) and alcohol. The gas helps the bread to rise.

Flow chart

A flow chart is a diagram of a sequence of events. It makes planning much easier and more effective. A flow chart can be quite simple, just showing the order in which to do a number of stages. These stages can be broken down into further flow charts showing each action in more detail, or adding details like quality control checks.

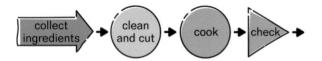

Food technologist

Food technologists work within the food industry. They help to develop new food products and study existing ones in order to meet consumer needs. The food and drink industry is the largest of the manufacturing industries in the UK.

Function

The function of a product means what it is intended to do. A snack is intended to provide a short burst of energy. A meal is intended to fill you up for some time. Some products may have more than one function. A yoghurt aimed at children may provide them with a tasty dessert but it will also help to meet their dietary needs for calcium.

Ingredients have functions, too. Each one has a special role in the production of a product, such as adding sweetness or making the product light.

Input

The input is part of a system. It is what is required to start the system, such as ingredients, money, workers, etc.

Mass production

This refers to the same food product being produced in very large quantities. For example, bread or biscuits need to be produced regularly to meet consumer demand. It is more efficient to have a large manufacturing plant producing them.

Multicultural

The UK is called a multicultural society because it is made up of people from a variety of cultures or backgrounds.

Over the years people have moved to the UK from all parts of the world and settled here, just as many British people have moved to other countries to live.

The UK has benefited from the influence of other cultures over the years. Today we take for granted many foods in our diet that were not traditionally British.

Non-starch polysaccharide (NSP)

This is the rather long name given to dietary fibre. Carbohydrate foods such as wholemeal flour, bran, oats, brown rice all provide NSP or dietary fibre which helps prevent constipation. NSP is also found in vegetables, fruit, nuts and seeds.

Nutrients

All food is made of nutrients. Different foods provide different amounts and types. The main nutrients are carbohydrate, fat, protein, vitamins and minerals. Our bodies need the correct balance of nutrients on a daily basis.

Nutritional value

The nutritional value of a food is the amount and type of nutrients it contains. Many food products have nutritional labelling stating the nutrients to be found in that food.

One-off production

This type of production is the exact opposite to mass production. One-off means one product is produced at a time. It is likely to be a quality product and probably expensive. It may be made to meet a consumer's specific needs. For example, making a celebratory cake for a special occasion.

Organoleptic qualities

These are the qualities or properties of a food that can be described during sensory analysis. Using our senses we can assess a food's appearance, texture, aroma and flavour.

Output

Every successful system will have an output! After going through all the necessary processes the output of a system might be a cake, a cook–chill meal or a bread product. In other words, it is the product produced by that system.

Preservation

This term is used to describe giving food a longer shelf-life. For example, fresh pastry will keep a few days if chilled but frozen pastry will keep in the freezer for months. Drying is another method of preservation (e.g. pasta). Foods preserved in different ways will keep for different lengths of time.

Preservatives

There is a list of permitted preservatives that can be used in the European Union. They each have a number with an E at the beginning. For example, E200 is a preservative called sorbic acid. Preservatives help to prolong the shelf-life of a food. Some may be naturally occurring. Information about preservatives and other additives can easily be found.

Process

A system has an input at the beginning, an output at the end and various processes in the middle. These processes evaluate the inputs to be changed to become outputs. Processes might include mixing, kneading, rolling, joining, baking, freezing, etc.

Product analysis

This is an activity that involves *taking apart* a food product. You do not literally have to take the food apart! The purpose is to find out more about a product, especially if you are going to design something even better.

You might read the information provided on the packet as this provides detail about the ingredients. The design of the packaging might show the target consumer group.

Preparing, cooking, looking, smelling and tasting all help to *disassemble* a product and tell you more about it.

Quality assurance

A manufacturer promises or guarantees their product is safe and meets a particular standard. This is known as quality assurance. The manufacturer is assuring the consumer that the product is of a good quality.

Season

All the fruits and vegetables you buy have a natural season. This is the time of year when they grow successfully in a particular country. When a fruit or vegetable is in season, it is likely to be at its cheapest and highest quality.

Shelf-life

This term refers to the length of time a food will be good to eat. Some foods have a very short shelf-life. For example, a fresh cream cake is best eaten on the day it is made. Other foods like flour and rice have a much longer shelf-life. The date mark on food products states how long foods can safely be kept before being eaten.

See also **Date marks**.

Fresh fish has a shelf-life of only a few hours. Pasteurised milk is safe for 3 to 4 days. Dried pasta will last a year. A can of baked beans has a shelf-life of up to four years.

Small scale

If food is being produced on a small scale it is being made in small quantities. A local bakery may make bread and cakes on a small scale to meet the needs of the local community.

Specification

A specification may be general for a range of products or just for one product. A specification gives the details of the product or product range. If it is a general specification then each product must match all the points in the range. For example, *must not contain animal products* would fit a range of vegetarian meals.

A **design specification** tells the food technologist about the type of product they should design (e.g. a frozen dessert).

A **product specification** must cover every detail a manufacturer would need to know to make that product. Details might include information about:

▶ type of ingredients
▶ quantity of ingredients
▶ portion size
▶ target consumer group
▶ method of making
▶ time taken to mix/knead/whisk
▶ size of ingredients after chopping/slicing/rolling out
▶ length of time for cooking/rising/chilling, etc.

Survey

A survey is an investigation of things people do and/or what they think and feel about certain things. Such information helps to identify the products they are most likely to need and want.

There are several ways this information might be gathered. One is to interview a small number of people individually, or hold a discussion group session (known as a *focus group*).

Another is to conduct a questionnaire. This enables a larger number of people to be surveyed. Questionnaires need to be planned and tested carefully if they are to produce information that is helpful and reliable.

Index